K. A. HESSE·

GRADED
ARITHMETIC PRACTICE

BOOK THREE

Longman

LONGMAN GROUP UK LIMITED
Longman House, Burnt Mill,
Harlow, Essex CM20 2JE, England
and Associated Companies throughout the world

© K. A. Hesse 1962
Decimal and Metric Edition © Longman Group Ltd 1970

First published 1962
Decimal and Metric edition first published 1970
Seventeenth impression 1987

Pupils' edition ISBN 0 582 18169 0
Teachers' edition ISBN 0 582 18170 4

Produced by Longman Group (FE) Ltd
Printed in Hong Kong

Write answers only:

A	$8p - 5p =$	$7p + 3p =$	$4p + 7p =$	$5p + 6p =$
B	$7p - 4p =$	$9p - 6p =$	$11p - 5p =$	$13p - 8p =$
C	$15p - 6p =$	$9p + 7p =$	$8p + 9p =$	$8p + 10p =$
D	$3p \times 3 =$	$4p \times 5 =$	$7p \times 4 =$	$6p \times 5 =$
E	$16p \div 4 =$	$21p \div 7 =$	$30p \div 6 =$	$42p \div 7 =$
F	$\frac{1}{2}$ of 12 g $=$	$\frac{1}{2}$ of 20 cm $=$	$\frac{1}{3}$ of 15 mm $=$	$\frac{2}{3}$ of 18 mm $=$
G	$\frac{1}{2}$ of 100 $=$	$\frac{1}{2}$ of £1 $=$	$\frac{1}{4}$ of £1 $=$	$\frac{1}{2}$ of 50p $=$
H	$6 \text{ cm} \times 7 =$	$8 \text{ cm} \times 8 =$	$7 \text{ cm} \times 9 =$	$9 \text{ cm} \times 8 =$
I	$27 \text{ kg} \div 9 =$	$36 \text{ kg} \div 12 =$	$72 \text{ m} \div 9 =$	$84 \text{ hr.} \div 7 =$
J	$48 \text{ hr.} \div 6 =$	$60 \text{ hr.} \div 12 =$	$96 \text{ m} \div 12 =$	$63 \text{ m} \div 9 =$
K	30 minutes $=$	hour	30 seconds $=$	minute
L	$1\frac{1}{2}$ minutes $=$	seconds	3 weeks $=$	days
M	12 hours $=$	day	$\frac{1}{2}$ kilogramme $=$	grammes
N	$\frac{1}{2}$ kilometre $=$	metres	250 millilitres $=$	litre
O	$\frac{1}{2}$ centimetre $=$	millimetres	$\frac{1}{2}$ metre $=$	centimetres
P	50 centimetres $=$	metre	$\frac{1}{2}$ metre $=$	millimetres
Q	4 tens $=$	fives	1 fifty $=$	fives
R	2 tens $=$	twos	£3 $=$	fifties
S	14 twos $=$	tens	twos	9 fives $=$	tens	five
T	6 tens $=$	fives	£2 $=$	fives
U	100 millilitres $=$	litre	2 litres $=$	millilitres
V	10 fifties $=$	pounds	7 cm 8 mm $=$	millimetres

State in figures the value of the figure six in each of these numbers:

A   1 607   2 786   6 400   167   3 060
B   4·36   16·04   50·6   0·68   5·06

Write in words

C   3 094   17·6

D   24·65   4·08
E   25 809

Write as decimals

F   five units, three tenths and two hundredths
G   eight point nought seven

Add (+)

H   32   67   43   957   496   589
         14   85   60   147   778   437
         56   54   98   806   609   984

Subtract (−)

I   74   50   87   324   600   538
       − 34   − 26   − 39   − 108   − 537   − 199

Multiply (×)

J   52   69   87   509   967   345
       × 4   × 3   × 6   × 7   × 9   × 12

Divide (÷)

K   3)609   5)303   8)600   9)9010   11)2156

Measure these lines, giving the answer first in millimetres and then in centimetres and millimetres

A _____   _____

B _____   _____

C _____

State which measurement you would use, kilometres, metres or millimetres to measure each of these lengths

D The length of a match   the thickness of a pencil

E The length of a river   the length of a street

F The distance between lamp-posts   the distance between cities

G A journey to the seaside   the length of a garden

Complete

H $\frac{1}{2}$ km =   metres 2 km =   metres $\frac{1}{2}$ m =   centimetres

I 25 cm =   metre 5 mm =   cm 200 cm =   metres

J $\frac{1}{5}$ km =   metres $\frac{2}{5}$ km =   metres $\frac{2}{5}$ m =   centimetres

K $\frac{1}{5}$ cm =   mm 4 mm =   cm $\frac{1}{2}$ cm =   millimetres

Write the first answer as a fraction and the second as a decimal

L 1 mm =   cm or   cm   3 mm =   cm or   cm

M 6 mm =   cm or   cm   9 mm =   cm or   cm

N 11 mm =   cm or   cm   17 mm =   cm or   cm

O 29 mm =   cm or   cm   53 mm =   cm or   cm

Write in columns and add

P 2·3 cm + 1·6 cm + 2·2 cm   3·1 cm + 0·8 cm + 4·3 cm

Q 1·4 km + 4·5 km + 3·4 km   0·5 m + 3·3 m + 5·7 m

Write in columns and subtract

R 6·7 mm − 3·4 mm   7·2 cm − 4·8 cm   5·3 km − 0·8 km

S 20·2 m − 8·4 m   20 km − 7·6 km   0·81 m − 0·57 m

REVISION OF MONEY

4

Write what you should add to each of these amounts to equal 2 tens
A 3 fives, a two and a one   2 fives, 2 twos and a one
B I five, 4 twos and 3 ones   3 fives and a two

Write what change you should receive from a fifty after paying
C 3 tens, a five and a two   2 tens, 2 fives and 6 ones
D 4 tens, a five and 2 twos   I ten, 7 fives and 2 twos

Complete
E How many 20ps equal £1?   How many 10ps equal £1?
Write as pence
F £1·26 =   £3·70 =   £0·94 =   £0·90 =
Write as pounds
G 256p =   140p =   83p =   10p =
Write as figures
H five pounds sixty-four   thirty pounds eight

Add (+)

I					
12p	23p	14p	32p	14p	25p
25p	8p	40p	20p	37p	9p
14p	20p	19p	19p	8p	30p

J					
£2·13	£4·25	£2·47	£0·37	£23·43	£4·06
1·45	0·63	0·62	4·06	7·08	0·87
2·54	3·42	4·73	0·25	15·81	0·09

Subtract (−)

K					
82p	40p	69p	72p	93p	80p
− 57p	− 27p	− 35p	− 38p	− 79p	− 39p

L					
£4·29	£5·03	£0·70	£0·82	£0·70	£2
− 2·70	− 3·07	− 0·53	− 0·67	− 0·36	− 0·60

Add (+)

A	215	387	609
	387	260	84
	609	53	307

Subtract (—)

B	520	813	706
	−413	−790	− 98

Multiply (✕)

C	347	975	286
	✕ 5	✕ 8	✕ 12

Divide (÷)

D   6)304   9)901   11)210

Write as centimetres and millimetres

E   1·4cm   1·7cm   3·0cm   4½cm

Write as centimetres

F   1cm 2mm   4cm 9mm   26mm   35mm

Write in columns and add

G   3·7cm + 0·5cm + 6·6cm   4cm + 5·8cm + 0·7cm

Write in columns and subtract

H   4·7cm − 1·4cm   3·5cm − 0·8cm   10cm − 5·7cm

Write as pence

I   £1·32   £1·06   £0·70   £0·17   £0·08

Write as pounds

J   43p   9p   240p   60p   102p

Write in columns and add

K   £2·13 + £1·07 + £3·92   £3·64 + £1·80 + £0·09

Write in columns and subtract

L   £27·36 − £9·44   £7·10 − £3·25   £2·40 − £0·48

EXTENDING NUMBER COMBINATIONS Work across the page

Add (+)

A	$9+3=$	$2+8=$	$4+5=$	$3+7=$	$8+0=$
B	$6+4=$	$2+9=$	$5+6=$	$9+4=$	$6+7=$
C	$9+5=$	$6+9=$	$8+7=$	$7+9=$	$8+9=$
D	$11+2=$	$12+5=$	$13+4=$	$12+8=$	$14+5=$
E	$15+6=$	$17+3=$	$12+9=$	$14+7=$	$16+8=$
F	$17+8=$	$19+6=$	$18+7=$	$19+9=$	$20+6=$
G	$21+3=$	$23+5=$	$22+8=$	$24+5=$	$26+4=$
H	$23+7=$	$25+6=$	$24+7=$	$23+8=$	$25+7=$
I	$26+5=$	$23+9=$	$25+8=$	$22+9=$	$19+8=$
J	$25+9=$	$26+8=$	$24+9=$	$28+5=$	$27+6=$

Subtract (−)

K	$5-3=$	$6-2=$	$4-4=$	$7-5=$	$6-3=$
L	$7-4=$	$8-5=$	$5-0=$	$9-2=$	$8-6=$
M	$8-3=$	$9-6=$	$9-4=$	$8-7=$	$9-3=$
N	$11-8=$	$12-9=$	$11-3=$	$9-5=$	$12-4=$
O	$12-5=$	$13-4=$	$13-9=$	$14-5=$	$11-7=$
P	$13-5=$	$12-7=$	$14-6=$	$13-6=$	$12-8=$
Q	$14-8=$	$13-7=$	$14-7=$	$13-8=$	$15-6=$
R	$15-9=$	$14-9=$	$15-7=$	$15-8=$	$16-7=$
S	$17-8=$	$16-8=$	$16-10=$	$17-10=$	$11-9=$
T	$18-10=$	$17-9=$	$18-9=$	$19-10=$	$16-9=$

Complete

U	$2+3=12-$	$5+2=11-$	$3+6=16-$
V	$13-4=15-$	$14-6=17-$	$16-9=5+$
W	$15-7=2+$	$17-9=18-$	$3+5=13-$

SPEED PRACTICE

Add (+)

A	$19+1=$	$19+0=$	$20+1=$	$19+2=$	$21+1=$
B	$20+2=$	$19+3=$	$22+1=$	$21+2=$	$20+3=$
C	$19+4=$	$23+1=$	$23+3=$	$21+3=$	$20+4=$
D	$19+5=$	$21+4=$	$22+2=$	$22+3=$	$20+5=$
E	$22+4=$	$19+6=$	$20+6=$	$21+5=$	$24+1=$
F	$23+2=$	$19+7=$	$19+8=$	$20+7=$	$21+6=$
G	$24+0=$	$24+2=$	$25+0=$	$25+1=$	$24+3=$
H	$23+4=$	$19+9=$	$20+8=$	$20+9=$	$22+5=$
I	$19+0=$	$21+7=$	$21+8=$	$22+6=$	$22+7=$

J	580	368	579	698	854	479	658
	176	477	98	639	979	908	99
	68	199	378	708	799	679	876

K	124	231	400	352	435	265	354
	233	106	251	375	464	373	478
	115	412	130	284	943	97	807
	625	504	219	308	375	508	693

L	202	342	465	375	489	378	508
	734	685	256	136	705	687	399
	686	759	887	908	389	450	776
	855	486	549	697	990	879	588

M	177	63	558	1040	1764	2653
	324	697	41	2607	2055	1097
	577	48	89	1098	2979	3804
	989	769	689	3899	1889	1078

2*

SUBTRACTION

Subtract (—)

A	5 — 3 =	7 — 4 =	6 — 2 =	8 — 3 =	9 — 3 =
B	9 — 5 =	4 — 4 =	9 — 6 =	7 — 5 =	8 — 6 =
C	10 — 7 =	11 — 5 =	8 — 5 =	11 — 4 =	11 — 8 =
D	12 — 10 =	12 — 4 =	13 — 4 =	13 — 9 =	14 — 5 =
E	12 — 5 =	13 — 5 =	12 — 7 =	13 — 6 =	13 — 7 =
F	12 — 8 =	13 — 8 =	14 — 6 =	14 — 8 =	14 — 7 =
G	15 — 6 =	15 — 9 =	14 — 9 =	15 — 7 =	15 — 8 =
H	16 — 7 =	17 — 8 =	10 — 10 =	11 — 10 =	13 — 10 =
I	16 — 8 =	16 — 10 =	14 — 10 =	15 — 10 =	16 — 9 =
J	17 — 9 =	18 — 10 =	17 — 10 =	19 — 10 =	18 — 9 =

Subtract (—)

K	326 − 218	507 − 109	600 − 290	4103 − 1780	7864 − 5097
L	6476 − 3278	4527 − 1898	3055 − 1299	4706 − 1809	3767 − 1999
M	3393 − 595	3604 − 2976	5003 − 957	7542 − 6668	1043 − 978
N	1356 − 977	7000 − 991	5076 − 1078	6043 − 989	8008 − 7009
O	1005 − 909	2006 − 1099	4007 − 3909	8000 − 7995	1870 − 999

Write answers only

A   What is the total of eleven, nine and twelve?

B   What will be the new total if 73 is increased by nine?

C   Subtract nine apples from sixteen apples.

D   Reduce the sum of twelve and eight by nine.

E   Find the difference between twenty-one and twelve.

F   How many fowls are there altogether if there are 12 hens in one crate, 8 in another and 9 in another?

G   How many pencils are there in a box if 23 of the pencils are blue and 9 are red?

H   If there are 17 blue pencils and eight red pencils, how many must I add to the red ones to make as many as there are blue?

I   What number must be added to twelve cakes to make a total of twenty cakes?

Work out these sums

J   What is the total of 364, 708, 450 and 678?

K   Increase seven-hundred-and-sixty-eight by nine-hundred-and-thirty-four.

L   Find the difference between three-hundred-and-sixty-two and one-hundred-and-sixty-seven.

M   What must be added to four-hundred-and-thirty-four to make six-hundred-and-twenty-four?

N   How many more girls than boys are there in a school of two-hundred-and-eighty-three boys and three-hundred-and-twenty-one girls?

O   How many pupils are there in a school of one-hundred-and-eighty-nine girls and two-hundred-and-eleven boys?

P   By how many chickens can three-hundred-and-seventy-six be increased to make five-hundred chickens?

Q   What is the total when a farmer increases his flock of two-hundred-and-fifty-seven sheep by ninety-four sheep?

Write the time on these clocks in two ways

A  B  C  D

Write the time in figures if

E   Clock B was one hour fast.   Clock C was one hour fast.
F   Clock A was one hour slow.   Clock D was one hour slow.

Write answers only

G $\frac{1}{2}$ of 4 cakes = $\frac{1}{4}$ of 12 sweets =
H $\frac{1}{2}$ of 11p   = $\frac{1}{4}$ of 20 cm   =
I $\frac{1}{4}$ of 6p   = $\frac{1}{3}$ of 6p   =
J $\frac{1}{3}$ of 12 books = $\frac{2}{3}$ of 12 books =
K $\frac{2}{3}$ of 15 cm = $\frac{3}{4}$ of 16 apples =
L $\frac{3}{4}$ of 20 pens = $\frac{2}{3}$ of 24 desks =

Say how long each line will become if 1·7 cm is added

M   _____   _____
N   _____   _____

Say how long each line will become if 0·6 cm is taken off

O   _____   _____
P   _____   _____

Complete the following

Q   6 mm = of 12 mm   4 = of 12   5p = of a ten
R   50p = of £1   25p = of £1 $2\frac{1}{2}$ cm = of 5 cm

Say how much is not shaded on each of these drawings

A   B   C   D

By looking back at the drawings try to find the answers to these sums

E $\frac{1}{3}+\frac{1}{3}=$ $\frac{2}{3}+\frac{1}{3}=$ $\frac{1}{4}+\frac{1}{4}=$ $\frac{1}{2}+\frac{1}{2}=$ $\frac{1}{2}+\frac{1}{4}=$

F $\frac{2}{3}-\frac{1}{3}=$ $\frac{3}{4}-\frac{1}{4}=$ $\frac{1}{2}-\frac{1}{4}=$ $1-\frac{1}{2}=$ $1-\frac{3}{4}=$

G $\frac{2}{3}+\frac{2}{3}=$ $\frac{3}{4}+\frac{1}{4}=$ $\frac{1}{2}+\frac{3}{4}=$ $\frac{1}{3}+\frac{2}{3}=$ $\frac{3}{4}+\frac{1}{2}=$

H $\frac{1}{3}-\frac{1}{3}=$ $\frac{3}{4}-\frac{1}{2}=$ $\frac{2}{3}-\frac{2}{3}=$ $1-\frac{2}{3}=$ $1\frac{1}{3}-\frac{1}{3}=$

Complete

I   How many halves must be added to $\frac{1}{2}$ to make a whole one?

J   How many quarters must be added to $\frac{1}{4}$ to make a whole one?

K   How many thirds must be added to $\frac{1}{3}$ to make a whole one?

Say in figures how much of a whole cake is left if we cut away

L   one half   one quarter   one third   two halves

M   two quarters   two thirds   three quarters   three thirds

Which of these drawings shows by shading $\frac{1}{2}, \frac{1}{4}, \frac{1}{3}, \frac{2}{3}$?

N   O   P   Q

How many halves in

R   one apple?   two apples?   one-and-a-half apples?

How many quarters in

S   half-an-hour?   two hours?   one-and-a-half hours?

How many thirds in

T   one day?   three days?   one-and-two-thirds days?

Complete

A   21= tens +1   34= tens+4   62= tens+2

B   47= tens+   89= tens+   76= tens+

C   32+10=(tens+2)+ ten = tens+2=

D   45+10=(tens+)+ ten = tens+ =

E   73+10=(tens+)+ ten = tens+ =

F   34+20=(tens+)+ tens = tens+ =

G   27+20=(tens+)+ tens = tens+ =

H   43+30=(tens+)+ tens = tens+ =

I   23+10= tens+ =   45+20= tens+ =

J   34+10=   32+10=   32+20=   44+20=   67+30=

K   39+40=   68+30=   56+20=   49+40=   36+40=

L   25p+10p=   37p+20p=   63p+30p=   45p+20p=

M   48p+30p=   55p+40p=   36p+40p=   77p+20p=

N   34+12=(tens+4)+(ten+2)= tens+4+2=

O   43+21=(tens+3)+(tens+1)= tens+3+1=

P   37+21= tens+7+1= tens+ =

Q   55+14= tens+5+4= tens+ =

R   42+27= tens+ + = tens+ =

S   38p+21p=   41p+35p=   66p+23p=   75p+14p=

T   36+17= tens+(6+7)= tens+(1 ten+3)= tens+3=

U   28+26= tens+(8+6)= tens+(1 ten+)= tens+ =

V   47+23= tens+(+)= tens+(ten+)= tens+ =

W   69+27= tens+(+)= tens+(ten+)=

X   28+13=   47+24=   38+36=   69+23=   58+34=

Y   36p+26p=   45p+17p=   68p+27p=   39p+25p=

Z   54p+38p=   28p+32p=   49p+31p=   55p+38p=

Complete

A	23p+20p =	78p+20p =	42p+30p =	67p+30p =
B	47p+32p =	24p+32p =	67p+21p =	43p+25p =
C	28p+13p =	47p+26p =	38p+42p =	55p+36p =
D	59p+26p =	35p+47p =	69p+27p =	48p+45p =
E	36p+48p =	54p+29p =	48p+38p =	77p+18p =

F   83p+39p=(8 tens+)+(tens+)= tens+12= tens+2=

G   75p+46p=(tens+)+(tens+)= tens+ = tens+ =

H   67p+68p=(tens+)+(tens+)= tens+ = tens+ =

I   98p+45p= tens+13= tens+3= p=£

J   89p+58p= tens+ = tens+ = p=£

K   67p+73p= tens+ = tens+ = p=£

L   49p+68p= tens+ = tens+ = p=£

M 58p+49p= tens+ = tens+ = p=£

N   86p+25p= p=£   87p+25p= p=£

O   97p+14p= p=£   76p+54p= p=£

P   76p+45p= p=£   88p+32p= p=£

Q   68p+59p= p=£   57p+68p= p=£

R   87p+37p= p=£   96p+48p= p=£

S   93p+69p= p=£   78p+52p= p=£

T	40p+56p =	60p+40p =	58p+30p =	p=£
U	37p+45p =	26p+67p =	47p+38p =	p=£
V	58p+39p =	37p+59p =	76p+24p =	p=£
W	67p+35p =	48p+67p =	83p+27p =	p=£
X	48p+66p =	75p+88p =	68p+59p =	p=£
Y	36p+79p =	86p+59p =	71p+99p =	p=£
Z	79p+68p =	68p+88p =	97p+89p =	p=£

A $30-27=$ 27 up to 30 $=$ $40-35=$ 35 up to 40 $=$

B $60-53=$ up to $=$ $70-64=$ up to $=$

C $80-71=$ up to $=$ $50-43=$ up to $=$

D $20p-14p=$ $20p-17p=$ $20p-12p=$ $20p-16p=$

E $70p-66p=$ $70p-62p=$ $50p-44p=$ $80p-78p=$

F $80p-74p=$ $90p-83p=$ $90p-85p=$ $60p-52p=$

G $60p-57p=$ $40p-38p=$ $40p-37p=$ $70p-64p=$

H $90p-82p=$ $30p-26p=$ $30p-23p=$ $90p-83p=$

I $50-40=$ $50-20=$ $50-10=$ $50-30=$

J $50-10=$ $50-30=$ $50-40=$ $50-20=$

K $50-38=$ (38 up to 40) and (40 up to 50) $=$ and $=$

L $50-27=$ (27 up to) and (up to 50) $=$ and $=$

M $50-16=$ (16 up to) and (up to 50) $=$ and $=$

N $50-12=$ (12 up to) and (up to) $=$ and $=$

O $50-21=$ (up to) and (up to) $=$ and $=$

P $50-33=$ 7 and $=$ $50-18=$ and 30 $=$

Q $50-26=$ and $=$ $50-35=$ and $=$

R $50-14=$ and $=$ $50-22=$ and $=$

S $50p-40p=$ $50p-39p=$ $50p-37p=$ $50p-32p=$

T $50p-20p=$ $50p-18p=$ $50p-15p=$ $50p-17p=$

U $50p-30p=$ $50p-26p=$ $50p-21p=$ $50p-23p=$

V $50p-10p=$ $50p-4p=$ $50p-38p=$ $50p-46p=$

W $50p-23p=$ $50p-37p=$ $50p-15p=$ $50p-22p=$

A	19p − 15p =	17p − 8p =	20p − 13p =	19p − 12p =
B	20p − 12p =	20p − 13p =	25p − 22p =	35p − 31p =
C	45p − 42p =	65p − 61p =	95p − 93p =	85p − 84p =
D	50p − 43p =	70p − 67p =	85p − 82p =	80p − 72p =
E	55p − 52p =	60p − 52p =	70p − 63p =	40p − 31p =
F	60p − 54p =	35p − 33p =	90p − 87p =	30p − 26p =

G	100 − 78 = (78 up to 80) and (80 up to 100) =	and 20 =
H	100 − 83 = (83 up to) and (up to 100) =	and =
I	100 − 69 = (up to) and (up to 100) =	and =
J	100 − 45 = (up to) and (up to 100) =	and =
K	100 − 26 = (up to) and (up to) =	and =
L	100 − 65 = 5 and =	100 − 86 = and =
M	100 − 37 = and =	100 − 29 = and =
N	100 − 72 = and =	100 − 53 = and =
O	100 − 48 = and =	100 − 61 = and =
P	100 − 64 = and =	100 − 36 = and =

Q	100p − 92p =	100p − 89p =	100p − 87p =	100p − 83p =
R	100p − 75p =	100p − 72p =	100p − 66p =	100p − 68p =
S	100p − 41p =	100p − 48p =	100p − 57p =	100p − 53p =
T	100p − 29p =	100p − 26p =	100p − 24p =	100p − 25p =
U	100p − 35p =	100p − 38p =	100p − 31p =	100p − 34p =
V	100p − 73p =	100p − 54p =	100p − 85p =	100p − 47p =
W	£1 − 87p =	£1 − 96p =	£1 − 64p =	£1 − 33p =
X	£1 − 59p =	£1 − 42p =	£1 − 26p =	£1 − 72p =

State which of these amounts you could pay for with a 50p coin

A   20p   47p   39p   18p   67p   12p   40p   25p

State which of these amounts you could pay for with 2 tens

B   10p   25p   17p   12p   35p   16p   11p   9p

State which of these amounts you could pay for with 6 tens

C   50p   35p   55p   43p   66p   60p   51p   25p

State which of these amounts you could pay for with 4 tens and a five

D   50p   40p   41p   30p   60p   44p   54p   42p

State the values of three coins that would pay exactly for

E   7p   9p   21p   16p

F   25p   12p   17p   5p

G   70p   60p   £1·10   57p

State what is the smallest number of coins that would pay exactly for

     10p   15p   30p   8p   11p   17p   19p   25p
     40p   55p   53p   17p   65p   70p   88p   33p

State what change you should have from 2 tens when paying

J   18p   15p   19p   11p   20p   12p   16p   13p

State what change you should have from 3 tens when paying

K   28p   21p   25p   22p   27p   23p   26p   24p

State what change you should have from 2 twenties when paying

L   32p   38p   36p   40p   33p   35p   37p   31p

State what change you should have from a fifty when paying

M   47p   3p   40p   26p   5p   36p   12p   24p

N   15p   50p   23p   42p   34p   17p   25p   18p

State what change you should have from £1 when paying

A	90p	72p	44p	57p	33p	59p	46p	23p
B	41p	38p	66p	85p	27p	16p	34p	65p

State what change you should have from £2 when paying

C	£1·70	£1·50	£1·65	£1·28	£1·93	£1·17
D	£1·46	£1·81	£1·34	£1·60	£1·32	£1·61

Complete

E	26p+13p =	37p+14p =	58p+21p =	47p+25p =
F	53p+18p =	66p+27p =	45p+38p =	64p+29p =
G	37p+46p =	29p+36p =	76p+19p =	58p+38p =
H	66p+34p =	96p+16p =	87p+36p =	63p+59p =
I	72p+48p =	57p+59p =	66p+68p =	74p+67p =
J	55p+76p =	68p+77p =	49p+87p =	57p+89p =

Change to pence

K	£0·46	£1·07	£0·70	£1·23	£1·50	£2·03
L	£1·02	£0·80	£0·08	£0·05	£0·70	£0·09

Change to pounds

M	143p	106p	130p	56p	85p	40p
N	7p	17p	9p	108p	60p	110p

Complete

O	34p−18p =	27p−22p =	43p−35p =	50p−27p =
P	61p−37p =	80p−17p =	55p−28p =	83p−48p =
Q	94p−66p =	52p−26p =	76p−39p =	62p−19p =
R	£1−92p =	£1−76p =	£1−38p =	£1−24p =
S	£1−73p =	£1−44p =	£1−52p =	£1−61p =
T	£1−85p =	£1−29p =	£1−43p =	£1−37p =

THE FOUR RULES OF MONEY

Write answers only

A   What change should I receive from a twenty when paying for a box of matches which cost 15p?

B   How much should be paid for 3 seventeenpenny stamps?

C   What is the total cost of a writing pad at 48p, envelopes at 26p, and a bottle of ink at 47p?

D   What is the total cost of five handkerchiefs at 34p each?

E   Is 8p the correct change when paying for a handkerchief at 42p with a fifty?

F   If 8 pencils cost £1·60 what is the price of one pencil?

G   What sum of money is one quarter of three pounds?

H   What is the difference in cost between two chairs if one costs £57·34 and the other £58·10?

I   What sum of money is equal to ten fifties?

J   How much must be added to seven tens to make 2 pounds?

K   What should be paid for one peach if a box of nine costs £2·70?

L   If Tom has saved 37p how much will he have when his father gives him two tens and a five?

M   What should each of eight boys receive if they share two pounds amongst them?

N   How much had Peter if he had one fifty, four tens and two fives?

O   After paying 47p for a book Ann had 26p left.   How much had she at first?

P   Mary had saved £2·87 to buy presents for Mother and Father. If Father's present cost £1·39 what was the most that she could pay for Mother's present?

Q   What should 3 litres of oil cost if 5 litres cost £8?

R   At a Sale towels cost £2·27 instead of £2·33.   What did we save by buying four towels at Sale price?

many hours are there in one day?

many hours are there marked on a clock face?

ures what would be the time on this clock

e morning.

e afternoon.

ures

nty minutes past three o'clock in the afternoon.

nty minutes past three o'clock in the morning.

-past seven o'clock in the morning.

H half-past eleven o'clock in the evening.

I twenty-eight minutes past one o'clock in the afternoon.

J twenty-six minutes past twelve o'clock mid-day.

K twenty-minutes to twelve o'clock mid-day.

L five minutes past eight o'clock in the morning.

M seven minutes past three o'clock in the afternoon.

N nine minutes past twelve o'clock mid-day.

O half-past twelve o'clock midnight.

P two minutes past twelve o'clock midnight.

Q a quarter hour before noon.

R a quarter hour after midnight.

S three-quarters of an hour before midnight.

T forty-five minutes after noon.

U a quarter to seven o'clock in the morning.

V fifty minutes after eleven o'clock in the morning.

W fifteen minutes to twelve o'clock midnight.

Write what would be the correct time if this clock is

A 1 hour fast	**B** 20 minutes fast
C $\frac{1}{4}$ hour slow	**D** 25 minutes slow
E $\frac{3}{4}$ hour fast	

Give the time one hour after

F	4 p.m.	11.30 a.m.	12 noon
G	6.05 a.m.	1.45 p.m.	12 midnight
H	11 a.m.	11.30 p.m.	11.50 p.m.

Give the time one hour before

I	2.15 p.m.	5.30 a.m.	12 noon
J	12.30 p.m.	1.45 p.m.	12 midnight
K	1.30 a.m.	12.15 a.m.	11.45 p.m.

Give the time two hours before

L	10.18 p.m.	1 p.m.	2 a.m.
M	2 p.m.	1.45 a.m.	11.55 p.m.

Add one half-hour to

N	3.10 a.m.	11.30 a.m.	11.45 a.m.
O	12.18 p.m.	11.52 p.m.	12.48 a.m.
P	11.55 a.m. Tues.		11.55 p.m. Thurs.

Give the time one half-hour before

Q	1 a.m.	3.15 a.m.	11.45 p.m.
R	12.15 p.m.	12.25 p.m.	noon
S	12.05 a.m.	10.13 p.m.	midnight

Give the time 12 hours before

T	2.15 p.m.	10.35 p.m.	11.55 p.m.
U	7.30 p.m. Mon.		12.30 p.m. Wed.
V	8.45 a.m. Fri.		4.05 a.m. Sat.

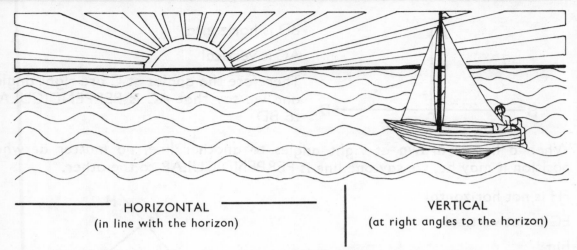

HORIZONTAL
(in line with the horizon)

VERTICAL
(at right angles to the horizon)

Use your dictionary to find the meaning of, "Out of plumb".

Which of these is a RIGHT ANGLE?

A   B   C   D   E   F   G

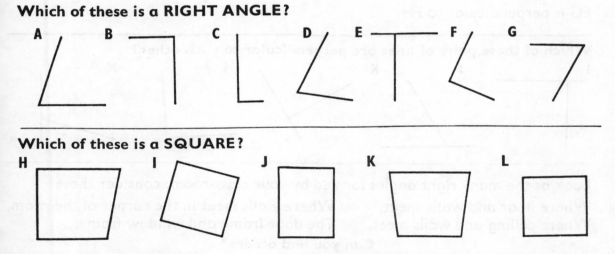

Which of these is a SQUARE?

H   I   J   K   L

Only a four-sided figure can enclose four right angles with straight lines. Any such four-sided figure having all its angles right angles is called a rectangle.

Which of these figures are RECTANGLES?

M   N   O   P   Q

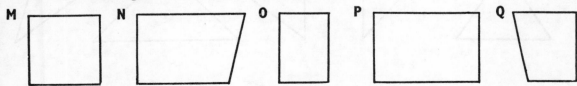

RIGHT ANGLES and TRIANGLES

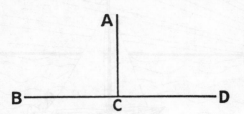

BD is horizontal

AC is vertical

Therefore the angles at C are right angles and we say that AC is PERPENDICULAR to BD.

When a line is drawn at right angles to another line, no matter at what position it may be, we say one line is PERPENDICULAR to the other.

FH is not horizontal

EG is not vertical

but

EG is at right angles to FH and therefore

EG is perpendicular to FH

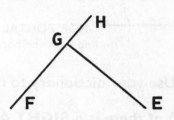

Which of these pairs of lines are perpendicular to each other?

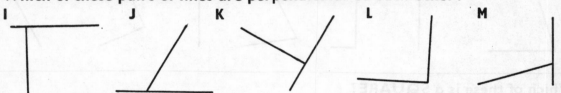

Look at the many right angles formed by your class-room: consider these:

Where floor and walls meet,

Where ceiling and walls meet,

Where walls meet in the corner of the room,

The door frame and window frames.

Can you find others?

Any figure having three straight sides is called a TRIANGLE.

Which of these triangles has no right angle?

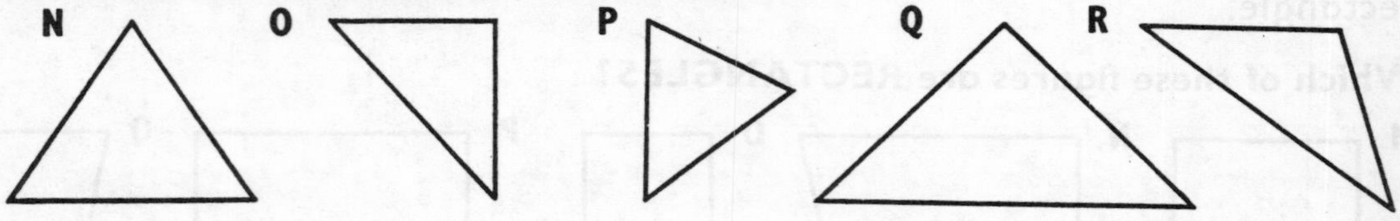

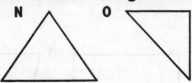

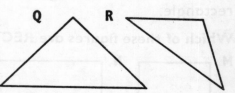

TABLE PRACTICE

Multiply (×)

A	4× 6=	5× 5=	6× 6=	8× 3=	3× 8=
B	6× 7=	3× 9=	4× 7=	5× 8=	7× 3=
C	7× 4=	5× 7=	6× 5=	7× 6=	8× 4=
D	9× 3=	10× 2=	6× 9=	7× 5=	11× 3=
E	10× 3=	9× 4=	12× 2=	3×12=	5×12=
F	4×11=	6×10=	7×12=	10× 4=	6× 8=
G	8× 7=	9× 6=	12× 8=	7×10=	8× 9=
H	11× 4=	12× 9=	7× 7=	12× 4=	12× 7=

Complete these sums

I	5× = 30	6× = 24	7× =56	6× = 60
J	10× = 50	8× = 40	× 6=48	× 9= 63
K	8× = 64	×10= 70	× 9=72	× 5= 45
L	× 7= 63	× 8= 72	8× =80	9× = 81
M	9× = 90	10× = 60	11× =55	× 6= 66
N	10× = 70	11× = 77	× 5=60	12× = 72
O	×12= 84	× 9= 90	× 8=88	×12= 96
P	12× =108	12× =144	10× =90	12× =120

Divide (÷)

Q	20÷ 5=	24÷ 4=	30÷ 6=	21÷ 7=	24÷ 8=
R	27÷ 9=	32÷ 8=	33÷11=	36÷ 9=	42÷ 6=
S	42÷ 7=	45÷ 5=	49÷ 7=	48÷12=	60÷ 5=
T	54÷ 6=	56÷ 7=	63÷ 9=	64÷ 8=	70÷10=
U	48÷ 8=	35÷ 7=	54÷ 9=	72÷ 6=	72÷ 9=
V	72÷12=	84÷12=	77÷ 7=	81÷ 9=	84÷ 7=
W	72÷ 8=	88÷11=	100÷10=	96÷12=	108÷12=
X	96÷ 8=	120÷10=	132÷11=	108÷ 9=	144÷12=

Complete

A (8×3)+ 4=   (7× 6)+ 5=   (9× 4)+ 3=   (6× 5)+ 4=
B (9×0)+ 2=   (8× 0)+ 3=   (5× 8)+ 6=   (8× 7)+ 5=
C (6×9)+ 3=   (5×10)+ 6=   (4×12)+ 5=   (12× 6)+ 9=
D (7×0)+ 8=   (12× 0)+10=   (8× 8)+ 7=   (9× 9)+ 8=
E (9×8)+ 7=   (12× 7)+ 8=   (8×11)+ 9=   (12× 8)+10=
F (12×9)+11=   (10×12)+ 0=   (11×11)+10=   (12×12)+11=

Multiply (×)

G
| 908 × 5 | 709 × 6 | 750 × 7 | 630 × 8 | 820 × 8 | 432 × 9 |

H
| 523 × 11 | 989 × 10 | 367 × 12 | 725 × 12 | 825 × 12 | 467 × 11 |

I
| 999 × 11 | 875 × 12 | 884 × 12 | 909 × 10 | 798 × 11 | 899 × 12 |

Work out these sums

J What number is equal to the product of six and seven-hundred-and-ninety?

K How many pints of milk are equal to 637 gallons?

L If each of nine crates holds one-hundred-and-fifty oranges what is the total number of oranges?

M What is the total quantity of bricks delivered by eight lorries if each carries 675 bricks?

N If there are twelve rows of seats in an open-air theatre, each row having one-hundred-and-nine seats, what is the total number of people that can be seated?

O Is the product of eight-hundred-and-seventy and nine, greater or less than the product of nine-hundred-and-seventy and eight?

SPEED PRACTICE

Divide (÷)

A	$18 \div 6=$	$27 \div 9=$	$21 \div 4=$	$27 \div 6=$	$27 \div 5=$
B	$26 \div 7=$	$26 \div 8=$	$30 \div 9=$	$30 \div 12=$	$30 \div 11=$
C	$37 \div 8=$	$41 \div 7=$	$52 \div 6=$	$51 \div 9=$	$57 \div 12=$
D	$62 \div 5=$	$70 \div 11=$	$66 \div 7=$	$69 \div 8=$	$71 \div 9=$
E	$75 \div 8=$	$80 \div 7=$	$85 \div 9=$	$79 \div 10=$	$83 \div 11=$
F	$84 \div 12=$	$91 \div 11=$	$93 \div 10=$	$87 \div 9=$	$94 \div 8=$
G	$102 \div 9=$	$103 \div 8=$	$111 \div 12=$	$108 \div 11=$	$117 \div 12=$

Divide (÷)

H $9\overline{)8101}$ $8\overline{)7210}$ $9\overline{)8153}$ $8\overline{)8090}$ $9\overline{)8190}$

I $9\overline{)8005}$ $10\overline{)1000}$ $11\overline{)1100}$ $10\overline{)9503}$ $11\overline{)4600}$

J $11\overline{)4708}$ $10\overline{)8061}$ $12\overline{)3050}$ $12\overline{)3333}$ $11\overline{)6006}$

K $10\overline{)9700}$ $12\overline{)4369}$ $12\overline{)4500}$ $11\overline{)3990}$ $12\overline{)5401}$

Write answers only

L   Into how many groups of three can you arrange 24 cakes?

M   How many times can eight be taken from forty-eight?

N   How many elevens are equal to seventy-seven?

O   Find how many children can have four cakes each from a tray containing forty-eight cakes.

P   Will nine divide exactly into eighty-three?

Q   What number is one-eighth of forty-eight?

R   How many boxes will be needed to pack one-hundred-and-eight peaches if each box holds twelve peaches?

SPEED PRACTICE

Divide (÷)

A	32 ÷ 7 =	41 ÷ 12 =	35 ÷ 9 =	50 ÷ 11 =	43 ÷ 10 =
B	62 ÷ 8 =	66 ÷ 10 =	71 ÷ 8 =	82 ÷ 12 =	61 ÷ 9 =
C	63 ÷ 11 =	93 ÷ 12 =	90 ÷ 11 =	88 ÷ 10 =	77 ÷ 8 =
D	84 ÷ 9 =	95 ÷ 10 =	106 ÷ 12 =	119 ÷ 12 =	109 ÷ 11 =

Divide (÷)

E
$$6\overline{)504} \qquad 8\overline{)900} \qquad 7\overline{)766} \qquad 9\overline{)815} \qquad 11\overline{)560}$$

F
$$11\overline{)3311} \qquad 9\overline{)2705} \qquad 7\overline{)6400} \qquad 8\overline{)9043} \qquad 12\overline{)4810}$$

G
$$10\overline{)5233} \qquad 9\overline{)7240} \qquad 11\overline{)1001} \qquad 10\overline{)1818} \qquad 12\overline{)1068}$$

H
$$12\overline{)2208} \qquad 12\overline{)5820} \qquad 11\overline{)9909} \qquad 12\overline{)7000} \qquad 10\overline{)1357}$$

Work out these sums

I   What number is one-sixth of three-thousand-and-sixty?

J   392 children are to travel in 7 coaches. How many children will there be in each coach?

K   How many nines are there in one-thousand-and-eighty?

L   A car takes 8 hours to travel 296 kilometres. How many kilometres is that for each hour of travelling?

M   A poultry farmer agrees to supply a large hotel with three-thousand dressed chickens during one year. How many is that for each month?

N   Which number should we have to multiply by eleven to make one-thousand-and-seventy-eight?

Write these shortened words in full

A   Fri.   Sat.   Tue.   Wed.

    Mon.   Sun.   Thu.

Write in full each day of the week in the correct order beginning with

B   Sunday,

Write how many days there are in

C   one week   two weeks   three weeks

Name the day which comes before

D   Wednesday   Saturday   Monday

Name the day which comes two days after

E   Sunday   Tuesday   Friday

Learn the order and how to spell the names of the months

January, February, March, April, May, June, July, August, September, October, November, December.

Name the month which comes after

F   January   August   November

    April   September   March

Name the month which comes before

G   July   November   March   June

    December   October   May   January

Name which month comes before and which comes after

H   February   May   October

Name which month is two months after

I   January   July   November

Look at this month's page of the Calendar

J   How many days are in this month?

K   Name the first day of the month.

L   Name the last day of the month.

M   On which day is the 3rd?   the 15th?   the 26th?

N   What is the date of the second Tuesday of the month?

O   What is the date of the last Friday of the month?

THE CALENDAR

Learn these facts and this poem

In one Year there are
365 days
52 weeks
12 Calendar months
but in a Leap Year
there are 366 days.

Thirty days hath September,
April, June and November.
All the rest have thirty-one,
Excepting February alone,
Which has twenty-eight days clear,
But twenty-nine each Leap Year.

Which of these were Leap Years?

A 1932   1940   1946   1950   1952   1962

Which of these will be Leap Years?

B 1970   1975   1980   1988   1990   1992

Which Leap Year

C   was the last?   will be the next?

How many days will there be in each of these months?

D   January   April   June
E   August   November   December
F   February 1974   February 1976   February 1978

If 1st June was on Wednesday give the date of these days in the same week

G   Friday   Tuesday   Sunday

If 1st July was on Thursday give the date of these days in the same week

H   Saturday   Tuesday   Sunday

Write how many days there are from

I   2nd Aug. to 10th Aug.   20th May to 30th May
J   25th Apr. to 2nd May   30th June to 15th July
K   20th Feb. '74 to 2nd Mar. '74   20th Dec. '72 to 10th Jan. '73

January is month No. 1.   Put the number against each of these

L   March   July   September   April   October   June

If "7.8.72" stands for "7 August 1972" write what is short for

M   3rd Feb. 1970   16th Aug. 1974   30th Dec. 1972
N   9th June 1971   31st Jan. 1975   23rd Mar. 1977
O   2nd May 1970   30th Nov. 1978   1st Sept. 1971

A	$3+5=$	$16+7=$	$9-6=$	$12-7=$	$23+9=$
B	$7\times3=$	$4\times8=$	$15\div5=$	$18\div9=$	$24\div3=$
C	$18-9=$	$32\div8=$	$7\times9=$	$12\times8=$	$54\div9=$
D	$9\times8=$	$12\times6=$	$64\div8=$	$96\div12=$	$9\times12=$
E	$17\div4=$	$33\div6=$	$50\div7=$	$56\div6=$	$60\div8=$
F	$80\div11=$	$60\div7=$	$85\div9=$	$102\div11=$	$112\div12=$

G $2\frac{1}{2}$ hours = half-hours $1\frac{3}{4}$ hours = quarter-hours

H Write the time that is one hour before noon.

I Write the time that is one half-hour after noon.

State in figures

J 5th June 1971 20th Mar. 1970 2nd Sept. 1972

State how many days there are from

K 23rd Feb. '72 to 3rd Mar. '72 25th Dec. '72 to 17th Jan. '73

Complete

L	$32p+20p=$	$48p+34p=$	$67p+26p=$	$38p+49p=$
M	$68p+40p=$	$57p+48p=$	$78p+58p=$	$69p+86p=$
N	$30p-23p=$	$50p-16p=$	$83p-58p=$	£1$-64p=$
O	$70p-62p=$	$81p-45p=$	$50p-27p=$	£1$-36p=$

Add (+)

P
```
 375    4268
 408     907
  96      85
 821    8769
```

Subtract (−)
```
 703    5701    8005
- 85   - 964   -7906
```

Multiply (×)

Q
```
 496      789
×   9    ×  12
```

Divide (÷)

$7)\overline{900}$ $9)\overline{5092}$ $11)\overline{1003}$

A Can you find 5 squares and 4 oblongs in this figure?

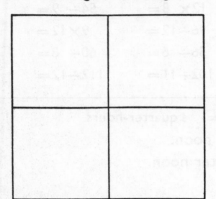

B Can you find 8 squares and 10 oblongs in this figure?

C Can you find 4 triangles in this figure?

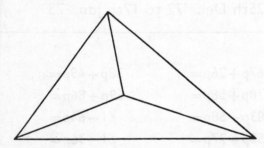

D Can you find 4 triangles in this figure?

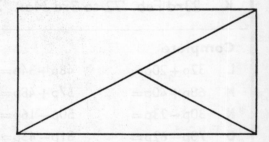

E Can you find 14 squares and 22 oblongs in this figure?

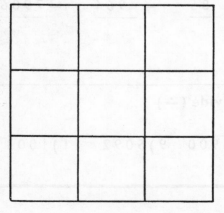

F Can you find 8 triangles in this figure?

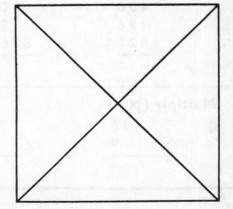

Here is a rectangle divided into four equal sections.

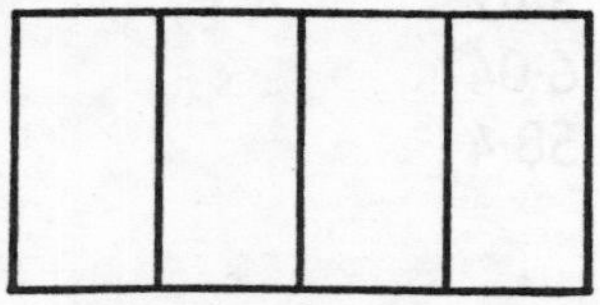

A How wide is each section?

B You draw a rectangle 48 mm by 20 mm and divide it similarly into four sections.

Say what length a rectangle would be if it were similarly divided into

C 3 sections of $\frac{1}{2}$ cm   5 sections of 7 mm   4 sections of $2\frac{1}{2}$ cm

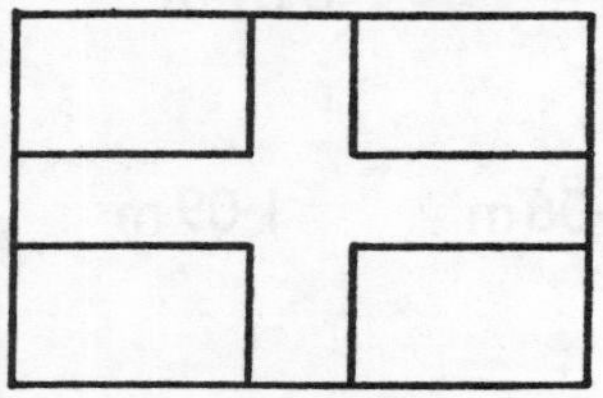

Here is the flag of St. George.

D You draw a similar flag, making all of your measurements twice the size of those in this drawing.

E Measure the length and width of the flag in the drawing above, and then work out the total distance round all the four sides.

The distance around any shape we call the PERIMETER.

Find the perimeter of each of these Rectangles and Triangles

F   **G** 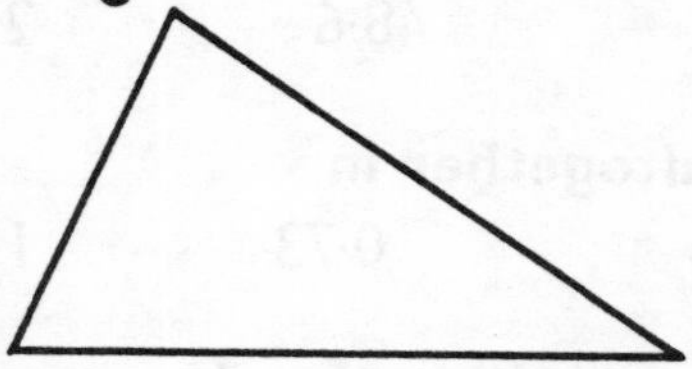   **H**

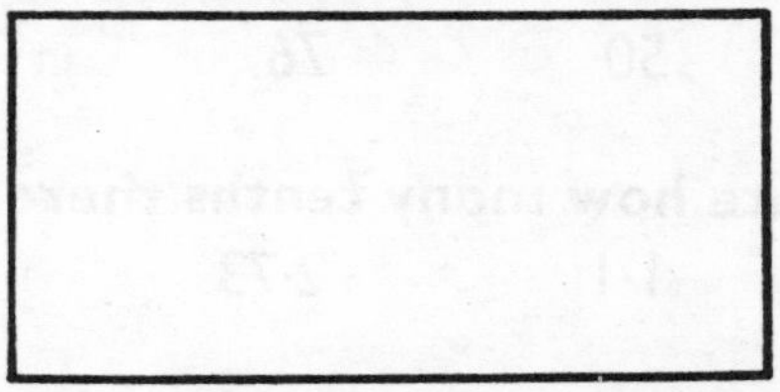

I 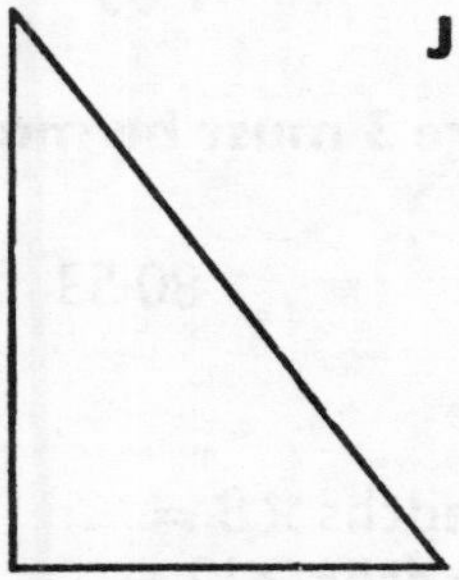   **J** 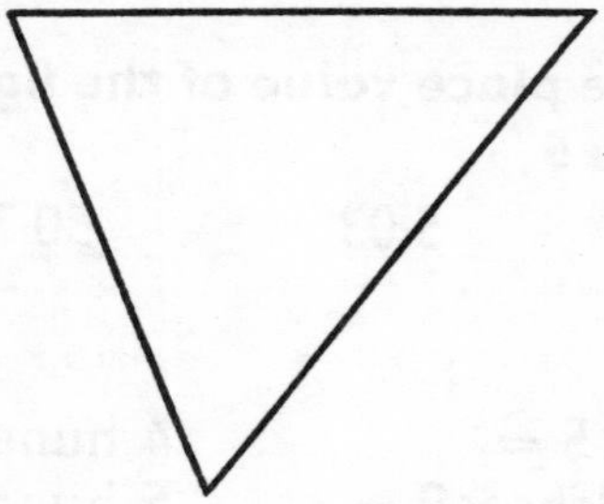   **K**

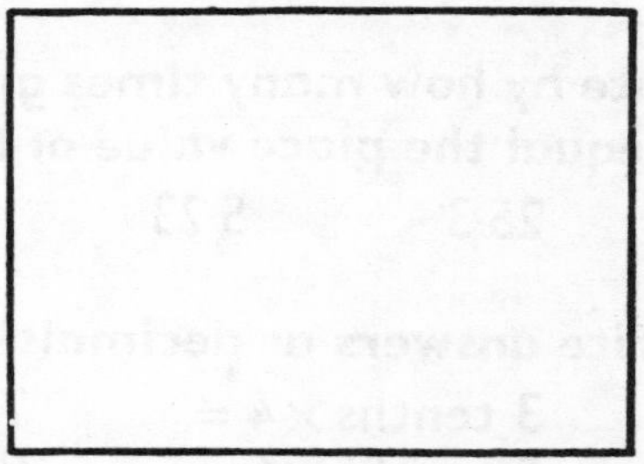

State the place value of the figure 4 in each number

A	342	3·42	34·2
B	406	40·6	6·04
C	584	5·84	58·4

Multiply each number by 10

D	8p	7 m	0·7 m	35p	2·06 l	50 g

Divide each number by 10

E	70p	£3	£0·20	0·6 m	1·37 g	0·81 m

Multiply each number by 100

F	2 m	0·2 m	0·02 l	£0·17	0·06 m	1·09 m

Divide each number by 100

G	£40	5 m	50p	£300	£270	7 l

State how many units there are altogether in

H	5	25	3·4	2·06	0·26	370

State how many tens there are altogether in

I	50	76	307	48·6	2·07	570

State how many tenths there are altogether in

J	1·1	2·73	10·6	0·73	1·08	2·01

State how many hundredths there are altogether in

K	0·07	0·14	0·76	0·8	1·12	1·05

State by how many times greater the place value of the figure 3 must be made to equal the place value of the figure 5

L	25·3	5·23	0·53	5·03	50·73	80·53

Write answers as decimals

M	3 tenths × 4 =	7 tenths × 5 =	4 hundredths × 8 =
N	5 tenths × 6 =	8 hundredths × 9 =	5 hundredths × 12 =

Write answers only

A	$5 \times 4 =$	$3 \times 6 =$	$6 \times 3 =$	$5 \times 6 =$	$6 \times 5 =$
B	$2 \times 7 =$	$7 \times 3 =$	$6 \times 6 =$	$4 \times 7 =$	$7 \times 4 =$
C	$8 \times 2 =$	$5 \times 7 =$	$8 \times 4 =$	$4 \times 8 =$	$5 \times 7 =$
D	$7 \times 6 =$	$9 \times 2 =$	$3 \times 9 =$	$9 \times 3 =$	$7 \times 6 =$
E	$5 \times 8 =$	$7 \times 7 =$	$8 \times 6 =$	$6 \times 8 =$	$4 \times 9 =$
F	$9 \times 4 =$	$10 \times 4 =$	$5 \times 11 =$	$9 \times 5 =$	$8 \times 8 =$
G	$3 \times 12 =$	$9 \times 6 =$	$6 \times 9 =$	$4 \times 12 =$	$12 \times 5 =$
H	$7 \times 9 =$	$5 \times 12 =$	$12 \times 6 =$	$11 \times 7 =$	$7 \times 12 =$

Complete:

I	$(4 \times 6) + 2 =$	$(3 \times 7) + 3 =$	$(8 \times 3) + 3 =$	$(9 \times 5) + 3 =$
J	$(7 \times 4) + 3 =$	$(6 \times 8) + 4 =$	$(9 \times 6) + 3 =$	$(8 \times 7) + 5 =$
K	$(5 \times 7) + 3 =$	$(7 \times 7) + 5 =$	$(8 \times 8) + 4 =$	$(9 \times 9) + 5 =$
L	$(6 \times 8) + 2 =$	$(3 \times 12) + 3 =$	$(12 \times 5) + 5 =$	$(6 \times 12) + 4 =$

Complete: under each answer re-write it in its true pound form

M	15p $\times$ 5	24p $\times$ 4	35p $\times$ 4	36p $\times$ 5	27p $\times$ 6	48p $\times$ 5	34p $\times$ 6
N	26p $\times$ 5	47p $\times$ 6	35p $\times$ 8	54p $\times$ 7	84p $\times$ 6	63p $\times$ 8	58p $\times$ 7
O	45p $\times$ 9	50p $\times$ 8	29p $\times$ 10	56p $\times$ 9	75p $\times$ 8	27p $\times$ 12	67p $\times$ 9
P	67p $\times$ 10	88p $\times$ 9	98p $\times$ 7	67p $\times$ 11	85p $\times$ 12	89p $\times$ 9	96p $\times$ 12

MULTIPLICATION OF POUNDS AND PENCE

Write answers only.   Work across the page

A	0·3 ×4=	0·2 ×6=	0·5 ×5=	0·7 ×8=
B	0·2 ×5=	0·5 ×8=	0·7 ×9=	0·8 ×5=
C	0·03×2=	0·04×2=	0·04×3=	0·06×4=
D	0·06×9=	0·07×6=	0·08×7=	0·09×9=

Multiply (×)

E
£1·32   £2·15   £1·63   £2·72   £3·16
×   4   ×   7   ×   6   ×   8   ×   9

F
£2·06   £3·09   £4·05   £1·75   £3·05
×   7   ×   8   ×   11   ×   8   ×   12

G
£5·60   £3·50   £6·09   £5·09   £4·78
×   5   ×   8   ×   9   ×   12   ×   9

H
£1·31   £1·24   £2·65   £1·86   £1·37
×   5   ×   6   ×   7   ×   6   ×   9

I
£0·64   £0·38   £0·87   £1·96   £2·89
×   10   ×   8   ×   9   ×   11   ×   12

J
£0·78   £6·08   £7·09   £5·80   £6·50
×   9   ×   7   ×   9   ×   12   ×   8

K
£1·08   £2·70   £1·90   £6·98   £1·09
×   8   ×   9   ×   11   ×   12   ×   12

Work across the page

A	$4 \times \_ = 12$	$5 \times \_ = 15$	$\_ \times 6 = 12$	$\_ \times 4 = 16$
B	$5 \times \_ = 20$	$6 \times \_ = 18$	$\_ \times 4 = 20$	$3 \times \_ = 18$
C	$4 \times \_ = 24$	$\_ \times 5 = 30$	$6 \times \_ = 36$	$\_ \times 6 = 36$
D	$7 \times \_ = 21$	$\_ \times 8 = 24$	$7 \times \_ = 21$	$\_ \times 3 = 27$
E	$9 \times \_ = 36$	$\_ \times 5 = 40$	$\_ \times 8 = 40$	$7 \times \_ = 42$
F	$\_ \times 6 = 48$	$8 \times \_ = 48$	$9 \times \_ = 45$	$6 \times \_ = 54$
G	$7 \times \_ = 56$	$\_ \times 7 = 49$	$3 \times \_ = 36$	$\_ \times 8 = 72$
H	$\_ \times 9 = 63$	$\_ \times 5 = 55$	$12 \times \_ = 48$	$\_ \times 5 = 60$
I	$12 \times \_ = 72$	$\_ \times 9 = 81$	$\_ \times 12 = 84$	$12 \times \_ = 108$

Take away: work across the page

J	$17 - 15 =$	$20 - 18 =$	$19 - 15 =$	$18 - 16 =$	$26 - 21 =$
K	$21 - 16 =$	$23 - 20 =$	$22 - 18 =$	$29 - 22 =$	$31 - 28 =$
L	$27 - 21 =$	$30 - 24 =$	$28 - 25 =$	$34 - 28 =$	$39 - 35 =$
M	$40 - 35 =$	$41 - 36 =$	$49 - 45 =$	$50 - 48 =$	$52 - 49 =$
N	$53 - 48 =$	$59 - 54 =$	$61 - 56 =$	$67 - 63 =$	$70 - 66 =$
O	$71 - 64 =$	$77 - 72 =$	$87 - 81 =$	$99 - 96 =$	$104 - 96 =$

Divide: work across the page

P	$16 \div 4 =$	$14 \div 6 =$	$21 \div 5 =$	$25 \div 3 =$	$34 \div 4 =$
Q	$15 \div 6 =$	$23 \div 7 =$	$25 \div 6 =$	$21 \div 8 =$	$31 \div 7 =$
R	$39 \div 5 =$	$40 \div 6 =$	$30 \div 8 =$	$30 \div 9 =$	$46 \div 8 =$
S	$56 \div 6 =$	$52 \div 8 =$	$45 \div 7 =$	$61 \div 8 =$	$41 \div 9 =$
T	$66 \div 10 =$	$57 \div 9 =$	$50 \div 11 =$	$60 \div 9 =$	$37 \div 12 =$
U	$53 \div 7 =$	$76 \div 8 =$	$73 \div 10 =$	$44 \div 12 =$	$66 \div 9 =$
V	$70 \div 12 =$	$63 \div 11 =$	$79 \div 9 =$	$79 \div 11 =$	$81 \div 12 =$
W	$91 \div 10 =$	$99 \div 12 =$	$93 \div 11 =$	$86 \div 9 =$	$105 \div 12 =$

A   1 unit =   tenths   3 units =   tenths

B   1 tenth =   hundredths   2 tenths =   hundredths

C   4 tenths =   hundredths   7 tenths =   hundredths

D   1·1 =   tenths   1·3 =   tenths

E   2·4 =   tenths   3·7 =   tenths

F   0·12 =   hundredths   0·18 =   hundredths

G   0·26 =   hundredths   0·43 =   hundredths

H   How many tens are there in £1 ?   £2?   £5?   £8?

I   How many pence are there in 1 ten?   3 tens?   6 tens?

Divide (÷)

J

$2\overline{)£2·52}$ $3\overline{)£4·26}$ $5\overline{)£6·15}$ $4\overline{)£6·12}$ $7\overline{)£9·24}$

K

$4\overline{)£4·24}$ $6\overline{)£6·36}$ $8\overline{)£10·64}$ $7\overline{)£10·08}$ $9\overline{)£11·07}$

L

$7\overline{)£8·47}$ $8\overline{)£9·76}$ $11\overline{)£13·31}$ $10\overline{)£13·50}$ $12\overline{)£15·12}$

M

$6\overline{)£12·48}$ $9\overline{)£27·54}$ $7\overline{)£17·50}$ $12\overline{)£22·80}$ $11\overline{)£15·40}$

N

$8\overline{)£1·76}$ $7\overline{)£2·59}$ $11\overline{)£2·53}$ $9\overline{)£3·96}$ $12\overline{)£4·20}$

O

$7\overline{)£3·01}$ $11\overline{)£4·07}$ $9\overline{)£3·06}$ $11\overline{)£6·05}$ $12\overline{)£10·08}$

P

$6\overline{)£0·54}$ $8\overline{)£0·96}$ $11\overline{)£0·88}$ $12\overline{)£1·08}$ $9\overline{)£0·81}$

In these sums remember we have two figures only after the point so you will have some remainders.   Write them as pence

A

$6)\overline{£7 \cdot 34}$ $5)\overline{£8 \cdot 26}$ $7)\overline{£9 \cdot 05}$ $9)\overline{£10 \cdot 11}$ $8)\overline{£10 \cdot 74}$

B

$8)\overline{£3 \cdot 55}$ $7)\overline{£3 \cdot 04}$ $9)\overline{£5 \cdot 00}$ $11)\overline{£4 \cdot 00}$ $12)\overline{£10 \cdot 06}$

C

$5)\overline{£3 \cdot 02}$ $8)\overline{£4 \cdot 06}$ $6)\overline{£4 \cdot 25}$ $9)\overline{£9 \cdot 56}$ $11)\overline{£7 \cdot 00}$

D

$6)\overline{£4 \cdot 40}$ $7)\overline{£3}$ $9)\overline{£6}$ $11)\overline{£8}$ $12)\overline{£30}$

E

$5)\overline{£8 \cdot 08}$ $6)\overline{£10 \cdot 05}$ $8)\overline{£11 \cdot 87}$ $9)\overline{£20 \cdot 50}$ $7)\overline{£20 \cdot 39}$

F

$7)\overline{£7 \cdot 68}$ $5)\overline{£20 \cdot 39}$ $9)\overline{£20 \cdot 77}$ $8)\overline{£30 \cdot 46}$ $11)\overline{£28 \cdot 68}$

G

$8)\overline{£3 \cdot 65}$ $7)\overline{£5 \cdot 00}$ $11)\overline{£9 \cdot 08}$ $9)\overline{£7 \cdot 00}$ $12)\overline{£19 \cdot 00}$

H

$6)\overline{£5 \cdot 01}$ $9)\overline{£6 \cdot 09}$ $8)\overline{£7 \cdot 90}$ $12)\overline{£10 \cdot 60}$ $11)\overline{£10 \cdot 30}$

I

$7)\overline{£2 \cdot 50}$ $8)\overline{£3 \cdot 60}$ $10)\overline{£2 \cdot 08}$ $11)\overline{£3 \cdot 40}$ $12)\overline{£6 \cdot 08}$

J

$9)\overline{£13}$ $11)\overline{£0 \cdot 86}$ $11)\overline{£8 \cdot 10}$ $12)\overline{£1 \cdot 50}$ $11)\overline{£23 \cdot 20}$

FRACTIONS

Look carefully at this frame and use it to find some of your answers

A WHOLE ONE									
$\frac{1}{2}$					$\frac{1}{2}$				
$\frac{1}{5}$		$\frac{1}{5}$		$\frac{1}{5}$		$\frac{1}{5}$		$\frac{1}{5}$	
$\frac{1}{10}$	$\frac{1}{10}$	$\frac{1}{10}$	$\frac{1}{10}$	$\frac{1}{10}$	$\frac{1}{10}$	$\frac{1}{10}$	$\frac{1}{10}$	$\frac{1}{10}$	$\frac{1}{10}$

A   How many fifths equal a whole one?

B   How many tenths equal a whole one?

C   Is there an exact number of fifths to equal a half?

D   How many tenths equal one half?

E   How many tenths equal one fifth?

Complete

F $\frac{1}{2}=\frac{}{10}$ $\frac{1}{5}=\frac{}{10}$ $\frac{2}{5}=\frac{}{10}$ $\frac{4}{5}=\frac{}{10}$ $\frac{3}{5}=\frac{}{10}$

G $\frac{1}{5}+\frac{1}{5}=$ $\frac{2}{5}+\frac{1}{5}=$ $\frac{1}{5}+\frac{2}{5}=$ $\frac{2}{5}+\frac{2}{5}=$ $\frac{3}{5}+\frac{1}{5}=$

H $1=\frac{}{2}$ $1=\frac{}{5}$ $1=\frac{}{10}$ $\frac{3}{5}+\frac{2}{5}=$ $\frac{4}{5}+\frac{1}{5}=$

I $\frac{1}{10}+\frac{1}{10}=$ $\frac{2}{10}+\frac{1}{10}=$ $\frac{4}{10}+\frac{3}{10}=$ $\frac{3}{10}+\frac{3}{10}=$ $\frac{5}{10}+\frac{2}{10}=$

J $\frac{1}{2}=\frac{}{10}$ $\frac{1}{5}=\frac{}{10}$ $\frac{1}{2}+\frac{1}{5}=$ $\frac{1}{2}+\frac{1}{10}=$ $\frac{1}{5}+\frac{1}{10}=$

K $\frac{2}{5}=\frac{}{10}$ $\frac{2}{5}+\frac{1}{10}=$ $\frac{1}{2}+\frac{2}{5}=$ $\frac{1}{2}+\frac{3}{10}=$ $\frac{2}{5}+\frac{1}{10}=$

L $\frac{1}{5}-\frac{1}{10}=$ $\frac{2}{5}-\frac{1}{10}=$ $\frac{1}{2}-\frac{1}{5}=$ $\frac{1}{2}-\frac{2}{5}=$ $\frac{3}{5}-\frac{1}{2}=$

M $1-\frac{1}{2}=$ $1-\frac{1}{5}=$ $1-\frac{3}{5}=$ $1-\frac{2}{5}=$ $1-\frac{3}{10}=$

N $\frac{4}{5}-\frac{3}{10}=$ $\frac{7}{10}-\frac{1}{2}=$ $\frac{3}{10}-\frac{1}{5}=$ $\frac{5}{10}-\frac{1}{2}=$ $\frac{4}{5}-\frac{1}{2}=$

Which is the greater?

O $\frac{3}{10}$ or $\frac{1}{5}$ $\frac{3}{5}$ or $\frac{1}{2}$ $\frac{4}{10}$ or $\frac{1}{2}$ $\frac{4}{10}$ or $\frac{3}{5}$ $\frac{9}{10}$ or $\frac{4}{5}$

High Town dep.:	07.15	09.30	10.45	11.50	13.10	16.20	18.35	22.05
Near Town	07.23	09.40	10.52	11.58	13.18	16.26	18.44	22.12
Middle Town	07.36	09.53	11.04	12.12	13.32	16.38	18.58	22.24
Low Town	07.52	10.10	11.20	12.30	—	16.52	19.16	22.40
Far Town arr.:	08.05	10.25	11.32	12.45	—	17.04	19.30	22.52

Write answers to the following questions

A High Town dep : Far Town arr. Write in full the words represented by 'dep.' and arr.'.

B Write in words the time at which the first train from High Town reaches Far Town.

C How long does it take the first train from High Town to reach Far Town?

D Which train leaves High Town before noon but arrives at Far Town after noon?

E At what time does the first train leave High Town after noon to reach Far Town?

F Write down in the same order of the time table how long it takes for each morning train to travel from High Town to Far Town.

G Looking at your answers to the previous sum write down the time at which the fastest morning train leaves High Town.

H Which is the fastest train from High Town to Near Town between 9 a.m. and Noon?

I Which is the fastest train from Middle Town to Far Town after 16.00 hours?

J Which is the latest train you may catch at Near Town to reach Low Town before 16.00 hours?

K Suppose you live at Far Town and that it takes a quarter-hour to travel home from the station. At what time would you reach home if you left High Town by the last train of the day?

Write answers only

A	67 sec. = min. sec.	75 sec. = min. sec.	96 sec. = min. sec.
B	72 min. = hr. min.	84 min. = hr. min.	98 min. = hr. min.
C	26 hr. = day hr.	30 hr. = day hr.	41 hr. = day hr.
D	48 hr. = days hr.	56 hr. = days hr.	64 hr. = days hr.
E	1 min. 12 sec. = sec.	1 min. 22 sec. = sec.	1 min. 35 sec. = sec.
F	1 hr. 17 min. = min.	1 hr. 27 min. = min.	1 hr. 38 min. = min.
G	1 day 8 hr. = hr.	1 day 13 hr. = hr.	1 day 22 hr. = hr.

Add (+)

H

min.	sec.	min.	sec.	min.	sec.	min.	sec.	min.	sec.
1	12	2	31	1	40	4	49	12	55
1	23	1	9		52	11	8		40
1	27	3	24	1	30	7	37	6	38

I

hr.	min.	hr.	min.	hr.	min.	hr.	min.	hr.	min.
1	17	2	15	10	18	5	47	7	49
3	45		52	5	54	10	8	14	50
1	26	3	8	12	7	6	53		38

J

wk.	days	wk.	days	wk.	days	wk.	days	wk.	days
2	4	7	6	4	5	13	6	15	5
3	0		5	21	0	4	0		6
4	5	3	5	6	6		5	8	4

K

days	hr.	days	hr.	days	hr.	days	hr.	days	hr.
2	8	4	13	5	21	13	22	3	21
1	7	2	10	10	20	6	9	15	18
3	9	1	8	3	5		20	6	7

TIME

Subtract (−)

A

min.	sec.		min.	sec.		min.	sec.		min.	sec.		min.	sec.
6	23		5	42		7	0		6	0		5	0
− 2	18		− 3	27		− 4	15		− 2	48		− 1	36

B

min.	sec.		min.	sec.		min.	sec.		min.	sec.		min.	sec.
4	15		6	26		15	17		12	32		25	40
− 2	20		− 3	44		− 10	53		− 8	45		− 16	48

C

hr.	min.		hr.	min.		hr.	min.		hr.	min.		hr.	min.
3	16		6	21		5	16		8	32		10	0
− 1	25		− 4	36		− 2	50		− 4	47		− 9	23

D

wk.	days		wk.	days		wk.	days		wk.	days		wk.	days
5	0		4	3		6	2		9	1		10	5
− 2	5		− 1	4		− 5	4		− 6	6		− 8	6

E

days	hr.		days	hr.		days	hr.		days	hr.		days	hr.
6	2		5	10		7	15		6	21		9	18
− 3	4		− 2	16		− 4	20		− 2	23		− 7	21

F

days	hr.		days	hr.		days	hr.		days	hr.		days	hr.
4	9		7	0		10	8		9	16		12	15
− 2	17		− 6	19		− 3	22		− 8	18		− 9	20

Work out these sums in your book

G What is the total time spent in school if morning school is from 8.55 a.m. to 12 noon, and afternoon school is from 1.25 p.m. to 4.00 p.m.?

H In crossing the Atlantic Ocean a liner took 7 days 6 hours. The return crossing took 5 days 17 hrs. How much quicker was the return trip?

FRACTIONS

Write what part of these circles is shaded

A   B   C   D   E

F How many halves in a whole one?

G How many halves in three whole ones?

H How many half-bars in five bars of chocolate?

I How many thirds in a whole one?

J How many thirds in two whole ones?

K How many third parts in four sticks of rock?

L How many quarters in two cakes?

M How many quarter apples in five apples?

N How many fifths in a whole one?

O How many fifth parts in three sticks of rock?

P How many fifth parts in six bars of chocolate?

Complete

Q $\frac{1}{2}$ of £1 = $\frac{1}{4}$ of £1 = $\frac{1}{5}$ of £1 = $\frac{2}{5}$ of £1 =

R $\frac{1}{2}$ of 1 hour = $\frac{1}{4}$ of 1 min. = $\frac{3}{4}$ of 1 min. = $\frac{3}{4}$ of 12 =

S $\frac{1}{3}$ of 1 hour = $\frac{2}{3}$ of 1 hour = $\frac{2}{3}$ of 15 = $\frac{2}{3}$ of 30p =

T $\frac{1}{5}$ of 20p = $\frac{2}{5}$ of 20p = $\frac{3}{5}$ of 40p = $\frac{4}{5}$ of 25p =

Complete

A	$\frac{1}{2}$ of 10 =	$\frac{1}{2}$ of 18 =	$\frac{1}{2}$ of 32 =	$\frac{1}{4}$ of 16 =
B	$\frac{1}{4}$ of 12 =	$\frac{3}{4}$ of 12 =	$\frac{3}{4}$ of 16 =	$\frac{3}{4}$ of 20 =
C	$\frac{1}{4}$ of 36 =	$\frac{3}{4}$ of 36 =	$\frac{3}{4}$ of 8 =	$\frac{3}{4}$ of 40 =
D	$\frac{1}{3}$ of 6 =	$\frac{1}{3}$ of 12 =	$\frac{2}{3}$ of 12 =	$\frac{2}{3}$ of 15 =
E	$\frac{1}{3}$ of 21 =	$\frac{2}{3}$ of 21 =	$\frac{2}{3}$ of 18 =	$\frac{2}{3}$ of 30 =
F	$\frac{1}{8}$ of 16 =	$\frac{1}{8}$ of 24 =	$\frac{1}{8}$ of 40 =	$\frac{1}{8}$ of 48 =
G	$\frac{1}{8}$ of 32 =	$\frac{3}{8}$ of 32 =	$\frac{5}{8}$ of 32 =	$\frac{7}{8}$ of 32 =
H	$\frac{3}{8}$ of 24 =	$\frac{3}{8}$ of 40 =	$\frac{5}{8}$ of 56 =	$\frac{7}{8}$ of 64 =

I   **Divide ($\div$)**   **Multiply ($\times$)**

$$4\overline{)£12\cdot68}$$

$$\begin{array}{r} £3\cdot17 \\ \times \quad\quad 3 \\ \hline \end{array}$$

J   What is $\frac{3}{4}$ of £12·68?

K	$\frac{1}{2}$ of £1·46 =	$\frac{1}{2}$ of 3·48 m =	$\frac{1}{2}$ of 7·68 l =
L	$\frac{1}{4}$ of £5·28 =	$\frac{3}{4}$ of £5·28 =	$\frac{3}{4}$ of £0·64 =
M	$\frac{1}{4}$ of £7·64 =	$\frac{3}{4}$ of £7·64 =	$\frac{3}{4}$ of £2·56 =
N	$\frac{1}{3}$ of 6·42 g =	$\frac{2}{3}$ of 6·42 g =	$\frac{2}{3}$ of 7·56 g =
O	$\frac{1}{5}$ of 7·65 m =	$\frac{2}{5}$ of 7·65 m =	$\frac{4}{5}$ of 7·65 m =
P	$\frac{3}{8}$ of 1 hr. 20 min. =	$\frac{5}{8}$ of 1 hr. 20 min. =	
Q	$\frac{2}{3}$ of 2 min. 45 sec. =	$\frac{3}{5}$ of 1 min. 40 sec. =	

Write what part of

R	1 hour are 20 minutes	1 minute are 15 seconds
S	1 minute are 45 seconds	1 hour are 45 minutes
T	1 hour are 40 minutes	1 minute are 12 seconds
U	2 hours are 30 minutes	2 hours are 40 minutes

THE FAMILY GROCER'S PRICE LIST

Bacon	£1·32 per ½ kg	Boiled ham	43p per 100 grammes
Butter	£1·12 per ½ kg	Cheese	£1·38 per ½ kg
Cocoa	£1·10 per tin	Corned beef	75p per ½ kg
	and 58p per tin	Coffee	£1·85 per tin
Currants	76p per ½ kg		and 95p per tin
Eggs	8p each	Jam	92p per 1 kg pot
Lard	55p per ½ kg		and 47p per ½ kg pot
Lemon curd	48p per pot	Margarine	63p per ½ kg
Marmalade	51p per pot	Minced beef	69p per 250 grammes
Mincemeat	56p per ½ kg	Ox tongue	53p per 100 grammes
Pressed beef	49p per 100 grammes	Raisins	83p per ½ kg
Sugar	47p per ½ kg	Sultanas	79p per ½ kg
Tea	£1·09 per ½ kg		

When paying a bill if there is a remainder, as ½ of 25p = 12p r 1p, the charge is taken to the next whole penny – 13p.

Say what change from five pounds I should receive if I buy

A ½ kg of bacon	1 doz. eggs	1 kg of cheese
B a large pot of jam	200 g of ox tongue	a large tin of coffee

Say what I should pay for ¼ kg of

C bacon	corned beef	lard
D cheese	raisins	sultanas
E boiled ham	minced beef	ox tongue
F pressed beef		jam

Say what I should pay for 1 kg of

G cheese	butter	sugar
H corned beef	sultanas	mincemeat

Say what I should pay for ½ kg of

I margarine	boiled ham	ox tongue
J minced beef	pressed beef	

Use the FAMILY GROCER'S PRICE LIST opposite

What change will there be from ten pounds after paying either of these bills?

A

Currants	$\frac{1}{2}$ kg
Raisins	$\frac{1}{2}$ kg
Sultanas	1 kg
total	
Change	

B

Jam	1 kg
Marmalade	1 pot
Sugar	$1\frac{1}{2}$ kg
total	
Change	

What change will there be from ten pounds after paying either of these bills?

C

Bacon	$\frac{3}{4}$ kg
Lard	$\frac{3}{4}$ kg
Pressed beef	200 g
total	
Change	

D

Tea	$\frac{1}{4}$ kg
Coffee—small	
Cocoa—large	
total	
Change	

What change will there be from a ten pound note after paying either of these bills?

E

Jam	$1\frac{1}{2}$ kg
Margarine	$\frac{1}{4}$ kg
Ox tongue	200 g
Minced beef	$\frac{1}{2}$ kg
Butter	$\frac{3}{4}$ kg
Eggs	4
total	
Change	

F

Currants	1 kg
Raisins	$\frac{1}{4}$ kg
Sultanas	$\frac{1}{2}$ kg
Lemon curd	2 pots
Tea	$\frac{1}{4}$ kg
Boiled ham	200 g
total	
Change	

Write the value in words and in figures of the 1 in each number

A   1 350
B   2 134
C   4 010
D   6 701
E   9 010
F   6 184
G   1 578

Notice: From A to D at each step the figure 1 moves one place to the right.
         From D to G at each step the figure 1 moves one place to the left.

H   As the place of a figure is changed to the right does the value increase or does the value decrease?

I   As the place of a figure is changed to the left does the value increase or does it decrease?

J   How many times greater is the 1 in C than that in D?

K   How many times less is the 1 in D than that in C?

L   How many times less is the 1 in E than that in F?

M   How many times less is the 1 in D than that in B?

N   How many times less is the 1 in D than that in A?

O   How many times less is the 7 in G than that in D?

Complete

P   To move a figure one place to the right makes it   times   .

Q   To move a figure two places to the right makes it   times   .

R   To move a figure three places to the right makes it   times   .

S   To move a figure three places to the left makes it   times   .

T   To move a figure one place to the left makes it   times   .

U   How many times greater is the value of the 3 in A than that in B?

V   How many times less is the value of the 4 in B than that in C?

A	Write in words:	0·01		
B	Write in words:	0·1		
C	How many hundredths in	0·1?	0·2?	0·5?
D	How many hundredths in	0·11?	0·21?	0·51?
		0·23?	0·67?	0·09?
E	Write in words:	0·1		1·0
F	How many tenths in	1? 2? 3? 7?		
		1·1? 2·1? 3·4? 7·6?		
G	How many hundredths in	0·01? 0·1? 1·0?		
		0·23? 0·4? 1·1?		
H	How many tenths in	0·7? 1·7? 0·17? 0·07?		
I	How many hundredths in	0·4? 0·04? 1·04? 0·44?		

Write these numbers in figures

J	1 unit and 3 tenths	one tenth and three hundredths
K	three hundredths	five tenths and six hundredths
L	seven hundredths	twenty-four hundredths
M	fifteen tenths	forty-seven hundredths
N	fifty-six tenths	thirty-eight hundredths

Complete

O	$0·08 + 0·03 =$	$0·07 + 0·04 =$	$0·07 + 0·06 =$
P	$0·06 + 0·08 =$	$0·17 + 0·05 =$	$0·19 + 0·03 =$
Q	$0·27 + 0·05 =$	$0·36 + 0·07 =$	$0·58 + 0·06 =$
R	$0·8 + 0·6 =$	$0·7 + 0·8 =$	$0·6 + 0·16 =$
S	$0·7 + 0·8 =$	$1·8 + 0·5 =$	$2·7 + 0·5 =$

A   What is the value of a figure one place to the right of units?

B   What is the value of a figure one place to the right of tenths?

C   What do you think we call the place value of figures to the right of hundredths?

If we make hundreds ten times greater we have thousands.

If we make hundredths ten times less we have thousandths.

We show thousandths by "th"

Look at this number:

Th	H	T	U	·	t	h	th
3	2	7	5	·	8	4	9

State the place value in words of the figures

D	2		5		4
E	3		8		9

How many thousandths in

F	0·006	0·016	0·008	0·018	0·028
G	0·043	0·143	0·243	0·627	0·081
H	0·027	0·207	0·516	0·82	0·93

Complete

I	0·008 + 0·004 =	0·009 + 0·003 =	0·007 + 0·005 =
J	0·006 + 0·009 =	0·007 + 0·008 =	0·018 + 0·003 =
K	0·017 + 0·006 =	0·018 + 0·005 =	0·016 + 0·004 =

Write these numbers in figures

L	two thousandths	four hundredths and six thousandths
M	twenty-two thousandths	six tenths and five thousandths
N	seventeen hundredths	eight tenths and three hundredths
O	nineteen thousandths	seven hundredths and four thousandths

We have a special way of showing thousandths when measuring.
One thousandth of a metre we call a millimetre.
One thousandth of a gramme we call a milligramme.
One thousandth of a litre we call a millilitre.

State how many millimetres there are in

A   0·007 metre   0·023 metre   0·067 metre   0·081 metre
B   0·032 metre   0·132 metre   0·216 metre   0·207 metre

State how many millilitres there are in

C   0·026 litre   0·145 litre   0·39 litre   0·68 litre

State how many milligrammes there are in

D   0·304 gramme   0·52 gramme   0·5 gramme   0·8 gramme

Complete

E   1·006 metre =   m   mm   1·062 litre =   l   ml
F   1·081 gramme =   g   mg   1·08 gramme =   g   mg
G   2·05 litre =   l   ml   3·5 metre =   m   mm
H   1·08 metre =   m   mm   2·8 litre =   l   ml
I   To change millimetres to metres we shall   by 1,000.
J   To change milligrammes to grammes we shall make the number   times less.
K   To change millilitres to litres we shall move the figure   places to the   and write the number as a decimal.

L   1,000 mm =   m   119 mg =   g   423 ml =   l
M   1,706 ml =   l   706 mm =   m   76 ml =   l
N   607 mg =   g   600 ml =   l   800 mm =   m
O   400 mm =   m   40 mm =   m   70 mg =   g
P   90 ml =   l   9 mm =   m   7 mm =   m
Q   1,007 mg =   g   3,070 ml =   l   5,500 mm =   m

Complete

A   To multiply by 1 000 we move figures   places to the
B   To divide by 1 000 we move figures   places to the

C	1 litre =	millilitres		0·5 litre =	millilitres	
D	1 metre =	millimetres		0·3 metre =	millimetres	
E	$\frac{1}{2}$ metre =	millimetres		$\frac{1}{2}$ litre =	millilitres	
F	0·234 m =	mm	0·306 g =	mg	0·278 g =	mg
G	0·86 l =	ml	0·73 l =	ml	0·69 l =	ml
H	0·075 m =	mm	0·032 m =	mm	0·048 m =	mm
I	1 litre =	ml	$\frac{1}{2}$ litre =	ml	$1\frac{1}{2}$ litres =	ml
J	1 metre =	mm	$\frac{1}{2}$ metre =	mm	$\frac{1}{4}$ metre =	mm
K	$\frac{1}{4}$ litre =	ml	$\frac{3}{4}$ litre =	ml	$\frac{1}{5}$ metre =	mm
L	0·706 m =	mm	0·37 litre =	ml	0·008 l =	ml
M	0·07 l =	ml	0·006 l =	ml	0·07 m =	mm
N	0·6 l =	ml	0·4 m =	mm	0·9 g =	mg
O	1 000 mm =	m	100 mm =	m	10 mm =	m
P	1 000 ml =	l	245 ml =	l	45 ml =	l
Q	1 000 mg =	g	307 mg =	g	48 mg =	g
R	356 ml =	l	56 ml =	l	93 ml =	l
S	409 mm =	m	9 mm =	m	6 mm =	m
T	560 mm =	m	870 ml =	l	240 mg =	g
U	400 mg =	g	600 mm =	m	800 ml =	l
V	208 ml =	l	8 ml =	l	7 mm =	m
W	90 mm =	m	9 mm =	m	5 ml =	l
X	700 mg =	g	50 mm =	m	300 mm =	m

Measure these lines and state your answer first as millimetres and then as centimetres and millimetres

A _____

B _____

C _____

Write as decimals in centimetres

D	1 cm 3 mm	1 cm 6 mm	2 cm 1 mm	1 cm 8 mm
E	3 cm 5 mm	2 cm 4 mm	1 cm 9 mm	3 cm 7 mm

Write in centimetres and millimetres

F	1·2 cm	2·8 cm	3·2 cm	1·5 cm
G	2·9 cm	4·3 cm	1·7 cm	5·6 cm

Write as centimetres

H	1·25 m	0·25 m	0·64 m	0·57 cm
I	0·5 m	1·5 m	0·08 m	0·09 m

Write as millimetres

J	1 m	1·327 m	0·357 m	0·307 m
K	0·261 m	0·061 m	0·082 m	0·82 m
L	0·76 m	0·8 m	0·9 m	0·09 m

Complete

M	1 l	=	ml	1·236 l =	ml	0·236 l =	ml
N	1 g	=	mg	0·348 g =	mg	0·609 g =	mg
O	0·286 g =		mg	0·086 g =	mg	1·086 g =	mg
P	0·329 g =		mg	1·029 g =	mg	1·02 g =	mg
Q	1·607 g =		mg	1·007 l =	ml	0·009 l =	ml
R	1·046 l =		ml	2·006 l =	ml	1·66 l =	ml
S	1·37 m =		mm	1·3 m =	mm	1·7 m =	mm
T	2·8 g	=	mg	1·08 g =	mg	0·008 l =	ml

Complete

A	To change metres to centimetres we	by	.
B	To change centimetres to millimetres we	by	.
C	To change litres to millilitres we	by	.
D	To change grammes to milligrammes we	by	.
E	To change millimetres to centimetres we	by	.
F	To change centimetres to metres we	by	.
G	To change millimetres to metres we	by	.
H	To change millilitres to litres we	by	.

Write as decimals in centimetres

I	1 cm 4 mm	1 cm 7 mm	9 mm	5 cm 8 mm	6 mm

Write as decimals in metres

J	1 m 37 cm	1 m 40 cm	2 m 76 cm	1 m 80 cm
K	1 m 30 cm	1 m 3 cm	1 m 8 cm	2 m 6 cm
L	3 m 96 cm	98 cm	70 cm	9 cm
M	1 m 20 cm	60 cm	6 cm	8 cm

Write as decimal quantities of metres, litres or grammes

N	1 m 342 mm =	1 m 765 mm =	1 m 806 mm =
O	1 l 255 ml =	2 l 305 ml =	1 l 350 ml =
P	1 g 750 mg =	1 g 800 mg =	1 g 600 mg =
Q	855 mg =	607 ml =	905 mm =
R	950 mm =	620 mm =	600 mm =
S	400 ml =	200 ml =	20 ml =
T	70 mm =	90 mg =	80 ml =
U	500 ml =	50 mm =	5 mm =

Write answers only.   Work across the page

A $7 \times 6 =$ $7 \times \quad = 56$ $8 \times \quad = 72$ $6 \times 9 =$ $5 \times 12 =$

B $16 + 5 =$ $12 - 7 =$ $13 - 8 =$ $14 + 7 =$ $23 + 8 =$

C $40 \div 8 =$ $51 \div 7 =$ $9 \times 8 =$ $9 \times \quad = 81$ $7 \times \quad = 84$

D $10 \times \quad = 100$ $12 \times \quad = 96$ $7 \times 9 =$ $21 - 6 =$ $43 + 7 =$

E $17 + 6 =$ $18 - 10 =$ $8 \times \quad = 64$ $12 \times \quad = 108$ $19 - 10 =$

F $60 \div 7 =$ $74 \div 9 =$ $80 \div 12 =$ $91 \div 8 =$ $110 \div 12 =$

Complete

G $60p + 45p = £$ $73p + 42p = £$ $56p + 48p = £$

H $71p + 59p = £$ $86p + 57p = £$ $78p + 39p = £$

I $80p - 73p = \quad p$ $70p - 64p = \quad p$ $50p - 22p = \quad p$

J $50p - 36p = \quad p$ $90p - 81p = \quad p$ $100p - 75p = \quad p$

K $£1 - 28p = \quad p$ $£1 - 66p = \quad p$ $£1 - 43p = \quad p$

L $\frac{1}{2}$ hr. after 12 noon is   40 min. before 12 noon is

M   12 hr. after 2.30 p.m. is   12 hr. before 4.50 p.m. is

N $\frac{1}{2}$ of 2 hr. 30 min. = $\frac{3}{4}$ of 1 hr. 20 min. =

O $\frac{1}{3}$ of 27 = $\frac{2}{3}$ of 27 = $\frac{1}{5}$ of 60 = $\frac{3}{5}$ of 35 =

P $\frac{5}{6}$ of 48 = $\frac{1}{8}$ of 96 = $\frac{3}{8}$ of 56 = $\frac{7}{8}$ of 72 =

Subtract (−)

Q $6211 - 5218$ $7006 - 909$

Multiply (×)

R 2006×7 4089×12 405×20

Add (+)

S   4305, 680, 5079, 836   6874, 96, 509, 68

Multiply (×)

T 134×16 507×23 860×35

Divide (÷)

U $6)\overline{403}$ $7)\overline{1010}$ $9)\overline{8001}$ $11)\overline{2090}$ $12)\overline{1190}$

GENERAL REVISION

A   If 1st July was on Thursday give the dates of these days in that week:
       Saturday   Wednesday   Monday

B   Which of these will be Leap Years?   1976   1980   1990

C   How many days are there from 25th May to 4th June?

Add (+)

D

£12·64	9·3 cm
£ 5·08	10·8 cm
£40·96	0·7 cm

Subtract (−)

E

£5·06	£3·80	5·62 m
− £3·86	− £0·93	− 2·83 m

Multiply (×)

F

38 p	£4·05	£1·80	£2·08	£4·09
× 7	× 8	× 11	× 5	× 12

Divide (÷)

G

9)£18·54   8)£2·74   7)£10·04   12)£30·08   11)£4·50

How many thousandths in

H   0·004   0·007   0·017   0·063   0·163   0·204

Write in figures

I   five hundredths   fifteen thousandths   nine thousandths

Complete

J	409 mm =	m	650 cm =	m	73 mm =	cm
K	200 mm =	cm	301 mm =	cm	301 mm =	m
L	300 ml =	l	750 mg =	g	1 900 ml =	l
M	0·623 m =	cm	0·623 m =	mm	0·086 l =	ml

Write answers only

A	$5+3=$		$8-5=$		$9-4=$		$5+4=$		$7+3=$
B	$11-5=$		$6+5=$		$8+7=$		$15-7=$		$13-8=$
C	$3\times4=$		$7\times2=$		$12\div6=$		$18\div3=$		$21\div7=$
D	$14+7=$		$15-6=$		$24\div8=$		$6\times7=$		$9\times8=$
E	$27\div9=$		$28\div4=$		$16+8=$		$18-9=$		$7\times8=$
F	$12\times3=$		$36\div9=$		$42\div7=$		$11\times7=$		$48\div6=$
G	$54\div9=$		$8\times12=$		$24+8=$		$56\div8=$		$63\div7=$
H	$33-7=$		$72\div9=$		$108\div12=$		$11\times12=$		$106\div9=$

Subtract (−)

I				
5602	4384	6512	4432	5093
− 804	− 395	− 505	−3997	− 998

Add (+)

J					
1898	1421	2324	1536	3114	5232
2905	2308	1643	3053	659	698
2587	1897	4788	968	875	9075
1598	3699	1579	2988	4787	856

Subtract (−)

K				
2006	5000	4793	8062	6002
−1807	−4996	−3695	− 994	− 599

Multiply (×)

L					
788	509	879	3080	5098	6089
× 9	× 12	× 11	× 7	× 11	× 12

Divide (÷)

M

$6\overline{)7002}$ $8\overline{)7096}$ $11\overline{)1067}$ $9\overline{)6208}$ $12\overline{)11700}$

Write answers only

A   In each of seven drums are five litres of oil.   How many litres of oil are there altogether?

B   A farmer has sheep in three fields.   In the first are 28, in the second are 9 and in the third are 7. How many sheep has the farmer altogether?

C   Jim began a game with 23 marbles but lost 8.   How many marbles had Jim at the end of the game?

D   Father is to plant two score cabbages.   How many rows will there be if he puts 8 in each row?

E   What is one-seventh of fifty-six?

F   How many $\frac{1}{2}$ litre tins can be filled from ten litres of paint?

Work out these sums in your book

G   From Monday to Friday the milkman delivered 268 bottles of milk daily. How many was that altogether?

H   There should be 324 children at school, but there are only 286 present. How many children are absent?

I   An aeroplane flies for seven hours at a steady speed of 348 km.p.h. How far does it travel?

J   If a plane has to travel 2 904 kilometres in eight hours, at what steady speed in km.p.h. must it fly?

K   A farmer has two-hundred-and-sixty-three sheep and decides to reduce the flock by one-hundred-and-seventy-five.   How many sheep will the farmer have then?

L   A poultry farmer had six-hundred-and-ninety-eight head of poultry and decides to increase the flock by two-hundred-and-seventy-five.   What head of poultry will the farmer have then?

M   What number is equal to one-ninth of 3 231?

N   If we reduce five-hundred-and-fifty-two by one-eighth what will be the new number?

SPEED PRACTICE

Multiply (✗)

A	$5\times 6=$	$7\times 4=$	$10\times 3=$	$12\times 2=$	$4\times 9=$
B	$3\times 12=$	$8\times 5=$	$4\times 11=$	$9\times 6=$	$4\times 12=$
C	$6\times 8=$	$7\times 8=$	$6\times 10=$	$11\times 7=$	$12\times 5=$
D	$8\times 8=$	$9\times 7=$	$10\times 8=$	$12\times 6=$	$7\times 12=$
E	$7\times 9=$	$12\times 8=$	$11\times 9=$	$10\times 11=$	$12\times 9=$
F	$9\times 8=$	$10\times 12=$	$9\times 9=$	$12\times 12=$	$11\times 12=$

Multiply (✗)

G
```
  123        305        234        506
×  10      ×  10      ×  20      ×  20
```

H
```
  340        670        230        170
×  10      ×  10      ×  20      ×  40
```

I
```
  125        204        105        306
×  20      ×  50      ×  40      ×  50
```

J
```
  123        216        152        217
×  21      ×  21      ×  31      ×  22
```

K
```
  164        217        232        254
×  23      ×  32      ×  16      ×  24
```

Multiply (X)

A
```
    206          107          306          208
  ×  23        ×  31        ×  14        ×  24
```

B
```
    230          140          270          160
  ×  21        ×  23        ×  32        ×  17
```

C
```
    135          245          126          144
  ×  32        ×  32        ×  25        ×  25
```

D
```
    235          145          325          216
  ×  23        ×  24        ×  42        ×  25
```

E
```
    305          205          105          406
  ×  33        ×  23        ×  24        ×  25
```

F
```
    205          472          308          505
  ×  26        ×  23        ×  15        ×  24
```

G
```
    135          307          294          405
  ×  28        ×  32        ×  35        ×  26
```

Multiply (×)

A
    453   578   496   387
×   22   ×   32   ×   42   ×   34

B
    305   408   379   480
×   18   ×   35   ×   26   ×   35

C
    260   506   408   687
×   35   ×   25   ×   52   ×   29

Work out these sums in your book

D   At a sports ground are 23 rows of seats, having 118 seats in each row. How many seats are there altogether?

E   A builder needed 575 blue bricks for each of 24 houses. How many blue bricks must be ordered?

F   What number is fifteen times larger than two-hundred-and-seven?

G   Find the product of three-hundred-and-forty-six and sixteen.

H   What number equals twenty-four times five-hundred-and-eight?

I   If a machine can fill 138 paper bags each hour, how many should it fill in seventeen hours?

J   A school is open for twenty-three days during the month. On each day 345 bottles of milk were delivered. What was the total number of bottles delivered to the school that month?

K   An aeroplane can fly at a steady speed of 325 km.p.h. If it could be kept flying for a whole day how far would it travel?

BILLS

How much must we pay to each tradesperson?

Baker

£

5 loaves of white bread @ 36p per loaf =
7 loaves of brown bread @ 34p per loaf =
6 swiss rolls @ 12p each =
Total

Coalperson

£

100 kilos of coal @ £6·50 per 50 kilos =
75 kilos of coke @ £6 per 50 kilos =
1 sack of logs @ £1·89 per sack =
Total

Milkperson

£

3 litres of milk @ 36p per litre =
1½ kg of butter @ £2·24 per kg =
6 eggs @ 9p each =
Total

Greengrocer

£

3½ kg of new potatoes @ 40p per kg =
½ kg of carrots @ 36p per kg =
2 lettuces @ 16p each =
1½ kg of apples @ 79p per kg =
Total

Butcher

£

1½ kg of beef @ £8·58 per kg =
½ kg of minced meat @ £2·81 per kg =
½ kg of sausages @ £1·45 per kg =
1½ kg of pork @ £3·06 per kg =
Total

How much must we pay altogether?

Complete

A   To make a number ten times greater we move the figures   place to the   .

B   To make a number one thousand times greater we move the figures   places to the   .

Change to metres, litres or grammes

C	1 kilometre = metres		$\frac{1}{2}$ kilolitre = litres		
D	$\frac{1}{2}$ kilogramme = grammes		$\frac{1}{4}$ kilometre = metres		
E	0·1 km = m	0·2 kl = l	0·3 kg = g		
F	0·236 kg = g	0·304 km = m	0·756 kl = l		
G	0·562 km = m	0·56 km = m	0·82 kg = g		
H	0·63 kg = g	0·6 kg = g	0·7 kl = l		
I	0·802 kl = l	0·8 kl = l	0·5 km = m		
J	0·02 kg = g	0·06 km = m	0·037 kg = g		
K	0·008 kl = l	0·009 kg = g	0·006 kl = l		
L	0·09 km = m	0·004 kl = l	0·9 km = m		

Write as kilos and metres, litres or grammes

M	1·125 kg = kg g		2·763 kl = kl l			
N	1·708 km = km m		3·75 kg = kg g			
O	3·95 kl = kl l		2·084 km = km m			
P	1·073 kg = kg g		4·08 kl = kl l			
Q	2·01 km = km m		7·09 kg = kg g			
R	4·7 kl = kl l		3·8 km = km m			
S	10·09 kg = kg g		6·5 kl = kl l			

Complete

A To change centimetres to metres we divide by ____ , which means moving the figures ____ places to the ____ .

B To change grammes to kilogrammes we divide by ____ , which means moving the figures ____ places to the ____ .

Change to kilos, stating all answers as decimals

C	1 000 l =	kl	500 m =	km	500 g =	kg
D	600 m =	km	607 l =	kl	640 g =	kg
E	308 g =	kg	901 m =	km	708 m =	km
F	200 g =	kg	20 l =	kl	60 l =	kl
G	90 m =	km	40 g =	kg	4 m =	km
H	8 l =	kl	9 m =	km	7 l =	kl
I	50 g =	kg	700 l =	kl	650 g =	kg
J	9 g =	kg	80 g =	kg	800 m =	km

Which is the greater or the greatest?

K 0·8 m or 0·80 m   0·07 l or 0·070 l   1·5 kg or 1·500 kg

L 2·005 km, 2·050 km or 2·500 km

Change to kilos, stating all answers as decimals

M	1 kg 576 g =	kg	2 kg 306 g =	kg	1 km 406 m =	km
N	2 kl 570 l =	kl	1 kl 680 l =	kl	2 km 190 m =	km
O	1 km 600 m =	km	3 km 300 m =	km	1 kg 900 g =	kg
P	2 kg 60 g =	kg	1 kg 80 g =	kg	3 kl 70 l =	kl
Q	3 kl 6 l =	kl	2 kl 9 l =	kl	1 km 8 m =	km
R	1 km 5 m =	km	3 km 40 m =	km	5 kg 90 g =	kg
S	2 kg 300 g =	kg	1 kl 30 l =	kl	4 km 7 m =	km

Write answers only.   Work across the page

A $0.2 \times 4 =$ $0.3 \times 4 =$ $0.6 \times 4 =$ $0.6 \times 5 =$

B $0.5 \times 2 =$ $0.4 \times 5 =$ $0.5 \times 6 =$ $0.5 \times 8 =$

C $1.2 \times 3 =$ $1.2 \times 7 =$ $0.8 \times 7 =$ $0.7 \times 9 =$

D $0.03 \times 3 =$ $0.03 \times 4 =$ $0.06 \times 4 =$ $0.08 \times 7 =$

E $0.14 \times 3 =$ $0.17 \times 5 =$ $0.05 \times 6 =$ $0.08 \times 5 =$

F $0.8 \times 9 =$ $0.5 \times 12 =$ $0.25 \times 8 =$ $0.15 \times 12 =$

Multiply (×)

G
$$\begin{array}{r} 2\cdot4 \\ \times\quad 2 \end{array} \qquad \begin{array}{r} 3\cdot5 \\ \times\quad 3 \end{array} \qquad \begin{array}{r} 5\cdot6 \\ \times\quad 6 \end{array} \qquad \begin{array}{r} 4\cdot7 \\ \times\quad 8 \end{array} \qquad \begin{array}{r} 6\cdot9 \\ \times\quad 7 \end{array} \qquad \begin{array}{r} 5\cdot8 \\ \times\quad 9 \end{array}$$

H
$$\begin{array}{r} 1\cdot14 \\ \times\quad 4 \end{array} \qquad \begin{array}{r} 2\cdot37 \\ \times\quad 5 \end{array} \qquad \begin{array}{r} 1\cdot68 \\ \times\quad 6 \end{array} \qquad \begin{array}{r} 2\cdot07 \\ \times\quad 5 \end{array} \qquad \begin{array}{r} 1\cdot09 \\ \times\quad 8 \end{array} \qquad \begin{array}{r} 2\cdot07 \\ \times\quad 9 \end{array}$$

I
$$\begin{array}{r} 1\cdot5 \\ \times\quad 2 \end{array} \qquad \begin{array}{r} 3\cdot5 \\ \times\quad 4 \end{array} \qquad \begin{array}{r} 2\cdot6 \\ \times\quad 5 \end{array} \qquad \begin{array}{r} 4\cdot8 \\ \times\quad 5 \end{array} \qquad \begin{array}{r} 5\cdot6 \\ \times\quad 5 \end{array} \qquad \begin{array}{r} 4\cdot5 \\ \times\quad 12 \end{array}$$

J
$$\begin{array}{r} 0\cdot16 \\ \times\quad 4 \end{array} \qquad \begin{array}{r} 0\cdot23 \\ \times\quad 6 \end{array} \qquad \begin{array}{r} 0\cdot47 \\ \times\quad 5 \end{array} \qquad \begin{array}{r} 0\cdot06 \\ \times\quad 5 \end{array} \qquad \begin{array}{r} 0\cdot05 \\ \times\quad 8 \end{array} \qquad \begin{array}{r} 0\cdot75 \\ \times\quad 12 \end{array}$$

K
$$\begin{array}{r} 0\cdot008 \\ \times\quad 4 \end{array} \qquad \begin{array}{r} 0\cdot016 \\ \times\quad 6 \end{array} \qquad \begin{array}{r} 0\cdot037 \\ \times\quad 8 \end{array} \qquad \begin{array}{r} 0\cdot065 \\ \times\quad 8 \end{array} \qquad \begin{array}{r} 0\cdot045 \\ \times\quad 12 \end{array}$$

L
$$\begin{array}{r} 1\cdot127 \\ \times\quad 8 \end{array} \qquad \begin{array}{r} 1\cdot216 \\ \times\quad 7 \end{array} \qquad \begin{array}{r} 1\cdot069 \\ \times\quad 9 \end{array} \qquad \begin{array}{r} 0\cdot786 \\ \times\quad 11 \end{array} \qquad \begin{array}{r} 1\cdot809 \\ \times\quad 12 \end{array}$$

DIVISION OF DECIMALS

Write answers only. Work across the page

A	$44 \div 2 =$	$4 \cdot 4 \div 2 =$	$0 \cdot 44 \div 2 =$	$0 \cdot 044 \div 2 =$
B	$12 \div 4 =$	$1 \cdot 2 \div 4 =$	$0 \cdot 12 \div 4 =$	$0 \cdot 012 \div 4 =$
C	$15 \div 5 =$	$1 \cdot 5 \div 5 =$	$0 \cdot 15 \div 5 =$	$0 \cdot 015 \div 5 =$
D	$4 \cdot 2 \div 6 =$	$0 \cdot 42 \div 6 =$	$0 \cdot 042 \div 6 =$	$0 \cdot 035 \div 7 =$
E	$2 \cdot 4 \div 8 =$	$0 \cdot 24 \div 8 =$	$0 \cdot 024 \div 8 =$	$0 \cdot 063 \div 9 =$
F	$0 \cdot 56 \div 7 =$	$0 \cdot 072 \div 9 =$	$0 \cdot 1 \div 2 =$	$0 \cdot 1 \div 5 =$
G	$1 \cdot 08 \div 9 =$	$1 \cdot 08 \div 12 =$	$0 \cdot 209 \div 11 =$	$0 \cdot 121 \div 11 =$

Divide (÷)

H

$2\overline{)3\,6}$ $\qquad$ $2\overline{)3 \cdot 6}$ $\qquad$ $2\overline{)0 \cdot 36}$ $\qquad$ $3\overline{)0 \cdot 45}$ $\qquad$ $5\overline{)0 \cdot 75}$

I

$4\overline{)5 \cdot 68}$ $\qquad$ $6\overline{)8 \cdot 04}$ $\qquad$ $7\overline{)9 \cdot 03}$ $\qquad$ $9\overline{)10 \cdot 35}$ $\qquad$ $8\overline{)9 \cdot 44}$

J

$5\overline{)16 \cdot 5}$ $\qquad$ $7\overline{)10 \cdot 5}$ $\qquad$ $6\overline{)14 \cdot 04}$ $\qquad$ $8\overline{)10 \cdot 08}$ $\qquad$ $11\overline{)17 \cdot 05}$

K

$3\overline{)15 \cdot 6}$ $\qquad$ $3\overline{)1 \cdot 56}$ $\qquad$ $4\overline{)1 \cdot 68}$ $\qquad$ $6\overline{)1 \cdot 44}$ $\qquad$ $5\overline{)2 \cdot 35}$

L

$4\overline{)1 \cdot 76}$ $\qquad$ $4\overline{)0 \cdot 176}$ $\qquad$ $5\overline{)0 \cdot 205}$ $\qquad$ $7\overline{)0 \cdot 329}$ $\qquad$ $8\overline{)0 \cdot 432}$

M

$5\overline{)1 \cdot 35}$ $\qquad$ $7\overline{)0 \cdot 707}$ $\qquad$ $9\overline{)0 \cdot 108}$ $\qquad$ $11\overline{)1 \cdot 001}$ $\qquad$ $12\overline{)1 \cdot 104}$

Divide (÷)

A

$5\overline{)1\cdot0}$ $7\overline{)2\cdot03}$ $6\overline{)0\cdot714}$ $9\overline{)0\cdot288}$ $8\overline{)0\cdot464}$

Change tenths remaining into hundredths to finish the answer

$2\overline{)2\cdot3}$ $4\overline{)13\cdot4}$ $5\overline{)10\cdot6}$ $5\overline{)12\cdot8}$ $8\overline{)10\cdot8}$

$2\overline{)0\cdot7}$ $5\overline{)30\cdot7}$ $8\overline{)16\cdot4}$ $6\overline{)30\cdot3}$ $12\overline{)48\cdot6}$

Change hundredths remaining into thousandths to finish the answer

$2\overline{)6\cdot45}$ $4\overline{)2\cdot62}$ $6\overline{)7\cdot05}$ $8\overline{)10\cdot04}$ $5\overline{)8\cdot04}$

$4\overline{)6\cdot14}$ $5\overline{)0\cdot82}$ $8\overline{)0\cdot92}$ $6\overline{)0\cdot51}$ $12\overline{)0\cdot42}$

Change tenths over into hundredths and hundredths over into thousandths to finish the answer

$2\overline{)7\cdot03}$ $4\overline{)0\cdot7}$ $8\overline{)0\cdot6}$ $8\overline{)3\cdot4}$ $12\overline{)3\cdot3}$

Take answers to the third decimal place

$8\overline{)77\cdot8}$ $5\overline{)1\cdot17}$ $7\overline{)3\cdot6}$ $9\overline{)4\cdot1}$ $11\overline{)1\cdot06}$

$6\overline{)0\cdot43}$ $7\overline{)6\cdot01}$ $11\overline{)8\cdot2}$ $9\overline{)6\cdot4}$ $12\overline{)10\cdot9}$

Write answers only

A	$\frac{1}{2}$ hour	=	minutes	$\frac{1}{4}$ minute =	seconds
B	45 minutes	=	hour	90 seconds =	minutes
C	a fortnight	=	days	48 hours =	days
D	3 minutes	=	seconds	3 days =	hours
E	26 weeks	=	year	75 minutes =	hours
F	August has		days	Feb. 1968 had	days

Add (+)

G

min.	sec.		hr.	min.		wk.	days		days	hr.
5	16		3	45		6	6		5	23
4	37			50		17	5			18
	23		7	9		9	6			9
2	58			38		28	4		3	21

Subtract (−)

H

min.	sec.		hr.	min.		wk.	days		days	hr.
15	10		6	23		5	4		3	17
− 9	18		−	56		− 3	6		− 2	21

Change to minutes   **Change to hours**

I	200 sec.	307 sec.	J	275 min.	440 min.

Change to days

K	77 hr.	103 hr.	176 hr.	235 hr.

Change to weeks

L	50 days	87 days	106 days	249 days

Multiply (×)

A

min. sec.	min. sec.	hr. min.	hr. min.	hr. min.
2 34	1 57	2 23	3 37	2 56
× 5	× 9	× 6	× 11	× 8

B

wk. days	wk. days	days hr.	days hr.	days hr.
3 5	5 6	2 11	3 17	4 21
× 10	× 12	× 7	× 9	× 12

Change to seconds

C

min. sec.	min. sec.
3 18	5 48

Change to minutes

D

hr. min.	hr. min.
4 37	6 56

Change to hours

E

days hr.	days hr.	days hr.	days hr.
2 16	4 19	3 23	7 18

Change to days

F

wk. days	wk. days	wk. days	wk. days
2 4	5 6	7 5	10 6

Divide (÷)

G

min. sec.	min. sec.	hr. min.	hr. min.
6)8 18	5)4 40	7)3 38	9)16 57

H

hr. min.	wk. days	wk. days	days hr.
11)9 54	10)14 2	12)9 6	8)9 16

I

days hr.	days hr.	days hr.	days hr.
7)5 13	9)14 15	11)10 18	12)21 0

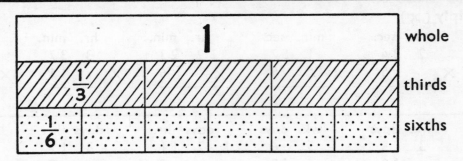

What are the missing figures?

A $1 = \frac{}{3}$ $\frac{1}{3} = \frac{}{6}$ $1 = \frac{}{6}$ $\frac{2}{} = \frac{1}{3}$

B $\frac{4}{6} = \frac{}{3}$ $\frac{1}{6} + \frac{1}{6} = \frac{1}{}$ $\frac{1}{3} + \frac{2}{3} =$ $\frac{2}{6} + \frac{2}{6} = \frac{}{2}$

C $1 - \frac{1}{3} = \frac{2}{}$ $1 - \frac{2}{3} =$ $\frac{1}{3} - \frac{1}{6} = \frac{1}{}$ $\frac{2}{3} - \frac{1}{6} = \frac{}{6}$

D $\frac{3}{6} + \frac{1}{6} = \frac{2}{}$ $1 - \frac{3}{6} =$ $\frac{1}{3} + \frac{1}{6} = \frac{3}{}$ $\frac{2}{3} - \frac{3}{6} =$

Write how many there are

E   thirds in $1,$ $2,$ $1\frac{1}{3},$ $2\frac{1}{3},$ $3\frac{2}{3},$ $4,$ $5\frac{2}{3},$

F   sixths in $\frac{2}{3},$ $1\frac{1}{6},$ $1\frac{1}{3},$ $1\frac{2}{3},$ $2\frac{1}{6},$ $3,$ $1\frac{5}{6},$

           $2\frac{1}{3},$ $3\frac{1}{3},$ $2\frac{5}{6},$ $3\frac{2}{3},$ $4\frac{1}{6},$ $5\frac{1}{3},$ $4\frac{2}{3}$

Which is bigger?

G $\frac{1}{3}$ or $\frac{1}{6}$ $\frac{1}{3}$ or $\frac{3}{6}$ $\frac{2}{3}$ or $\frac{3}{6}$ $\frac{2}{3}$ or $\frac{5}{6}$ $1\frac{1}{3}$ or $1\frac{1}{6}$

If possible write answers only

H $\frac{1}{3}$ of 6p = $\frac{1}{3}$ of 9p = $\frac{1}{3}$ of 12 kg = $\frac{1}{3}$ of 1 min. =

I $\frac{2}{3}$ of 6p = $\frac{2}{3}$ of 9p = $\frac{2}{3}$ of 12p   = $\frac{2}{3}$ of 1 hr. =

J $\frac{1}{6}$ of 6p = $\frac{5}{6}$ of 6p = $\frac{1}{6}$ of 18 m = $\frac{5}{6}$ of 18 m =

K $\frac{1}{6}$ of 18p = $\frac{5}{6}$ of 30p = $\frac{5}{6}$ of 36p = $\frac{5}{6}$ of 12 hr. =

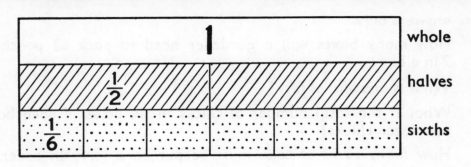

What are the missing figures?

A $1 = \frac{}{2}$ $\frac{1}{2} = \frac{}{6}$ $\frac{1}{2} - \frac{1}{6} = \frac{}{6}$ $\frac{1}{2} - \frac{2}{6} =$

B $\frac{1}{6} + \frac{1}{6} = \frac{2}{} = \frac{1}{}$ $\frac{2}{6} + \frac{1}{6} = \frac{3}{} = \frac{1}{}$

C $1 - \frac{1}{2} =$ $1 - \frac{1}{6} =$ $1 - \frac{3}{6} =$ $1 - \frac{5}{6} =$

Write how many there are

D   halves in   1,   2, $1\frac{1}{2}$, $2\frac{1}{2}$, $3\frac{1}{2}$, $7\frac{1}{2}$,   9,

E   sixths in $\frac{1}{2}$, $1\frac{1}{2}$, $\frac{1}{3}$,   2, $2\frac{1}{3}$, $2\frac{1}{2}$, $3\frac{1}{2}$,

Which is bigger?

F $\frac{1}{2}$ or $\frac{1}{6}$ $\frac{1}{2}$ or $\frac{2}{6}$ $\frac{1}{2}$ or $\frac{1}{3}$ $\frac{1}{2}$ or $\frac{5}{6}$ 1 or $\frac{7}{6}$

Put in order of size—biggest first

G $\frac{1}{6}, \frac{1}{2}, \frac{1}{3}$ $\frac{5}{6}, \frac{2}{3}, \frac{1}{2}$ $\frac{2}{3}, \frac{1}{2}, 1$

      $\frac{5}{6}, 1\frac{1}{3}, 1\frac{1}{2}$ $1\frac{1}{6}, 1\frac{1}{2}, 1\frac{1}{3}$

Work out these in your book

H   What must be added to one half to make a whole one?

I   What is one half of one third?

J   What must be added to one third to make one half?

K   What must be added to one half to make five sixths?

L   What must be added to one half to make two thirds?

M   What is one third of one half?

N   What is one third of one hour in minutes?

O   How many centimetres are there in one and a half metres?

Write answers only

A How many boxes will a gardener need to pack 63 peaches, putting 9 in a box?

B What is one fifth of fifty?

C What is the total number of chicks in six boxes if each box contains one dozen chicks?

D How many sacks of coke must be put on a lorry in order to deliver 8 sacks of coke to each of nine houses?

E A lorry can carry five tons. How many journeys must it make to remove sixty tons of bricks?

F Each of seven pupils is carrying eleven books. How many books are there altogether?

G From a ball of string nine pieces, each ten metres long, are cut. What is the total length used?

H One hundred tulips are to be put into bunches of ten. How many bunches will there be?

Work out these sums in your book

I It has been arranged for six 'buses to take 330 pupils on a school outing. How many will there be to each 'bus?

J A gardener wishes to plant 7 rows of bulbs with 45 in each row. How many bulbs must the gardener order?

K A machine makes two-hundred-and-fifty-six bricks per hour. How many does it make in a day of eight working hours?

L A packer has 9 crates into which 432 cauliflowers must be packed. How many should the packer put into each crate?

M How many tables will be needed to seat four-hundred-and-fifty pupils with room for 12 at each table?

N How many boxes, each holding 12 tennis balls, can be filled from 700 tennis balls?

O Find how many $\frac{1}{2}$ litre bottles of milk can be filled from 75 litres of milk.

Divide (÷)

A

$20\overline{)40}$ $20\overline{)60}$ $20\overline{)80}$ $30\overline{)60}$ $40\overline{)80}$

B

$21\overline{)42}$ $21\overline{)63}$ $21\overline{)84}$ $31\overline{)62}$ $41\overline{)82}$

C

$22\overline{)44}$ $22\overline{)66}$ $20\overline{)41}$ $20\overline{)61}$ $21\overline{)43}$

D

$30\overline{)63}$ $21\overline{)67}$ $22\overline{)46}$ $31\overline{)68}$ $22\overline{)90}$

E

$21\overline{)50}$ $21\overline{)71}$ $31\overline{)71}$ $20\overline{)47}$ $23\overline{)50}$

F

$20\overline{)100}$ $30\overline{)120}$ $50\overline{)150}$ $30\overline{)150}$ $20\overline{)140}$

G

$20\overline{)220}$ $21\overline{)231}$ $21\overline{)252}$ $20\overline{)420}$ $31\overline{)651}$

H

$21\overline{)483}$ $22\overline{)704}$ $31\overline{)372}$ $23\overline{)736}$ $32\overline{)416}$

Divide (÷)

A

$21\overline{)210}$ $20\overline{)400}$ $30\overline{)6003}$ $40\overline{)8406}$

B

$31\overline{)6820}$ $32\overline{)7042}$ $21\overline{)4644}$ $21\overline{)2228}$

C

$22\overline{)5060}$ $31\overline{)6300}$ $23\overline{)2420}$ $22\overline{)4510}$

D

$19\overline{)437}$ $29\overline{)1220}$ $18\overline{)1908}$ $28\overline{)1182}$

E

$18\overline{)3654}$ $17\overline{)5204}$ $27\overline{)2810}$ $38\overline{)7760}$

Work out these in your book

F   A motorist found that on a journey of 756 kilometres he had used 63 litres of petrol. How many km had he travelled for each litre of petrol used?

G   A bricklayer laid 2 160 bricks during 18 working hours. How many would that be for each working hour?

QUARTERS $\frac{1}{4}$ EIGHTHS $\frac{1}{8}$ SIXTEENTHS $\frac{1}{16}$

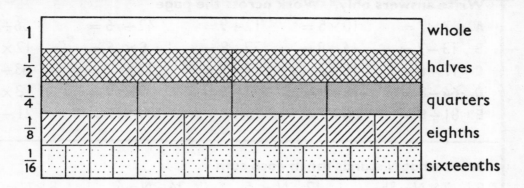

Which is the bigger number?

A $\frac{1}{2}$ or $\frac{1}{4}$ | $\frac{1}{2}$ or $\frac{1}{8}$ | $\frac{1}{16}$ or $\frac{1}{4}$ | $\frac{1}{8}$ or $\frac{1}{4}$

B $\frac{1}{8}$ or $\frac{3}{16}$ | $\frac{1}{4}$ or $\frac{3}{16}$ | $\frac{1}{4}$ or $\frac{3}{8}$ | $\frac{1}{2}$ or $\frac{3}{4}$

C $\frac{3}{8}$ or $\frac{5}{16}$ | $\frac{1}{2}$ or $\frac{9}{16}$ | $\frac{3}{4}$ or $\frac{5}{8}$ | $\frac{7}{8}$ or $\frac{11}{16}$

What are the missing figures? Use the diagram

D $\frac{1}{2}=\frac{}{4}=\frac{}{8}=\frac{}{16}$ | $1=\frac{4}{4}=\frac{}{16}=\frac{}{2}$

E $\frac{1}{2}=\frac{1}{4}+\frac{1}{}$ | $\frac{1}{2}=\frac{1}{4}+\frac{2}{}$ | $\frac{3}{8}+\frac{1}{8}=\frac{2}{}$

F $\frac{3}{8}+\frac{1}{8}=\frac{1}{}$ | $\frac{1}{16}+\frac{1}{16}=\frac{}{8}$ | $\frac{1}{16}+\frac{3}{16}=\frac{}{4}$

G $\frac{1}{4}=\frac{1}{}+\frac{1}{8}$ | $\frac{5}{16}=\frac{1}{4}+\frac{1}{16}$ | $\frac{1}{8}=\frac{1}{}+\frac{1}{16}$

H $\frac{3}{16}=\frac{1}{}+\frac{1}{16}$ | $\frac{3}{8}=\frac{1}{}+\frac{1}{8}$ | $\frac{3}{4}=\frac{1}{}+\frac{1}{4}$

I $\frac{1}{2}=\frac{}{8}$ | $\frac{1}{4}=\frac{}{16}$ | $\frac{1}{8}=\frac{}{16}$ | $\frac{1}{2}=\frac{}{4}$

J $\frac{3}{4}=\frac{}{8}$ | $\frac{3}{4}=\frac{}{16}$ | $\frac{3}{8}=\frac{}{16}$ | $\frac{7}{8}=\frac{}{16}$

K $1-\frac{1}{2}=$ | $1-\frac{1}{4}=$ | $\frac{1}{2}-\frac{1}{4}=$ | $\frac{1}{4}-\frac{1}{8}=$

L $1-\frac{3}{4}=$ | $1-\frac{5}{8}=$ | $1-\frac{9}{16}=$ | $\frac{1}{2}-\frac{3}{16}=$

Put in order of size—biggest first

M $\frac{1}{8}, \frac{1}{2}, \frac{1}{4}$ | $\frac{1}{8}, \frac{1}{2}, \frac{3}{16}$ | $\frac{1}{2}, 1, \frac{1}{4}$ | $1\frac{1}{2}, 1\frac{1}{16}, 1\frac{1}{8}$

N $\frac{1}{4}, \frac{1}{3}, \frac{1}{2}$ | $\frac{3}{8}, \frac{1}{2}, \frac{3}{4}$ | $1\frac{9}{16}, \frac{3}{4}, 1\frac{1}{2}$ | $\frac{1}{6}, \frac{1}{3}, \frac{1}{4}$

Write answers only. Work across the page

A	$7 \times 7 =$	$10 \times 5 =$	$12 + 9 =$	$42 \div 6 =$	$56 \div 7 =$
B	$13 - 7 =$	$14 - 8 =$	$72 \div 8 =$	$8 \times 5 =$	$12 \times 6 =$
C	$17 + 6 =$	$15 - 7 =$	$7 \times 9 =$	$12 \times 7 =$	$63 \div 9 =$
D	$64 \div 8 =$	$16 + 9 =$	$72 \div 8 =$	$9 \times 9 =$	$8 \times 12 =$
E	$81 \div 9 =$	$84 \div 7 =$	$23 + 8 =$	$100 \div 12 =$	$21 - 8 =$

State what N stands for in each sum

F	$7 \times N = 35$	$12 - N = 5$	$24 \div N = 4$	$8 \times N = 56$
G	$54 \div N = 6$	$13 + N = 22$	$63 \div N = 7$	$9 \times N = 108$

State the place value of the figure 7 in each of these numbers

H 2 704　　　　　　　　　37·26

I 5·607　　　　　　　　　290·7

Write these numbers in figures

J three hundred and seven　　　four thousand and nine

K five and four tenths　　　　one unit, and four hundredths

L six units and seventeen thousandths

M ninety and seven tenths

State how many tenths in

N	0·6	1·3	2·06	3·17	10·8	0·07

State how many hundredths in

O	0·23	0·08	0·172	1·06	1·109	0·008

State how many thousandths in

P	0·004	0·037	0·106	0·01	0·23	0·109

Write in figures

A   a quarter past eleven o'clock in the evening

B   the time three-quarters of an hour before mid-day

C   3rd Feb. 1965   31st Oct. 1962   17th May 1970

Give the time 24 hours after

D   9 p.m. 7th August

     11.45 a.m. 30th June

State how long it is from

E   11.35 a.m. to 1.10 p.m.

     9.30 p.m. to 7.50 a.m.

F   10.45 a.m. Monday to 3.20 p.m. Tuesday.

Add (+)

G	hr.	min.		min.	sec.		wk.	days		days	hr.		days	hr.
	7	38		4	50		4	6		2	7		6	18
		56		2	8			5		3	12			22
	3	9			47		3	6		1	5		5	9

Subtract (−)

H	wk.	days		days	hr.		days	hr.		min.	sec.		hr.	min.
	10	5		3	10		13	8		20	5		7	34
	− 3	6		− 2	15		− 5	19		− 18	43		− 4	57

Multiply (×)

I	wk.	days		days	hr.		days	hr.		min.	sec.		hr.	min.
	13	6		3	6		2	17		3	15		1	34
	×	5		×	6		×	8		×	9		×	14

Divide (÷)

J	wk. days	days hr.	days hr.	min. sec.	hr. min.
	9)12 6	7) 2 8	9)12 18	8)10 0	12)5 30

Work across the page

Add (+)

A					
3765	4839	52p	£6·37	1·07 cm	3·074 kl
408	78	8p	£0·86	12·6 cm	0·89 kl
6974	650	70p	£9·05	4·9 cm	7·6 kl
5089	947	19p	£7·48	14·85 cm	0·769 kl

Subtract (−)

B					
4006	8903	70p	£3·05	7·63 l	2·08 km
−3908	−5994	−38p	−£0·68	−0·95 l	−0·904 km

Multiply (×)

C					
305	4089	27p	£0·67	£2·06	0·609 m
× 8	× 12	× 9	× 11	× 12	× 12

Divide (÷)

D

9)816   7)5096   12)8500   8)£9·76   11)£13·53

E

5)84p   7)96p   9)£11·77   11)£5·60   12)£13·50

F

6)8·022   9)9·288   8)24·4   12)2·1   8)0·76

Multiply (✗)

G			
247	608	750
× 23	× 35	× 18

Divide (÷)

H

31)744   29)754

Write in columns and add.   Work across the page

A 3·7 m + 0·86 m + 12·7 m   16p + 9p + 80p

B £10·70 + £0·85 + £3·09   £7·63 + £0·84 + £0·09

Write in columns and subtract

C £10 − £3·24   £5 − 63p   4·07 l − 0·674 l

Complete

D	0·627 l =	ml	0·803 g =	mg	1·078 m =	mm
E	0·083 m =	mm	7·62 g =	mg	2·08 l =	ml
F	0·04 m =	mm	0·5 g =	mg	1·5 l =	ml
G	2·7 g =	mg	1·08 l =	ml	0·09 m =	mm
H	1·009 l =	ml	0·007 m =	mm	0·6 m =	mm

Write as decimals in metres, litres or grammes

I	1 m 27 cm =	2 m 304 mm =	1 m 8 cm =
J	2 l 470 ml =	3 g 500 mg =	2 g 250 mg =
K	3 m 85 cm =	3 m 75 mm =	1 l 750 ml =
L	2 g 90 mg =	5 l 800 ml =	3 m 80 cm =
M	4 l 8 ml =	7 m 6 cm =	10 g 90 mg =

Complete

N	1·62 m =	m	cm	1·326 m =	m	mm	1·62 m =	m	mm
O	2·085 l =	l	ml	7·5 g =	g	mg	5·06 g =	g	mg
P	1·627 l =	l	ml	1·36 m =	m	cm	3·7 m =	m	cm
Q	3·08 g =	g	mg	2·6 g =	g	mg	4·09 l =	l	ml
R	2·4 m =	m	cm	1·3 m =	m	mm	2·063 g =	g	mg
S	4·07 l =	l	ml	3·96 l =	l	ml	5·8 m =	m	cm

Complete

A $\frac{1}{4}$ of 16 hr. = $\frac{2}{5}$ of 30 min. = $\frac{3}{5}$ of $\frac{1}{2}$ metre =

B $\frac{5}{6}$ of 3 litres = $\frac{3}{8}$ of £1·12 = $\frac{3}{4}$ of 1 kilogramme =
                                                                          £

C $\frac{1}{4}$ kg of boiled ham @ £4·28 per kg   =
   $\frac{3}{4}$ kg of bacon @ £2·66 per kg   =
   $\frac{1}{4}$ kg of pressed beef @ £2·49 per $\frac{1}{2}$ kg   =
   9 eggs @ 9p each   =   ——
                              total   =   ——

Work in your book

D Find the change from £10 when paying the bill in C.

E What must be added to 37·8 metres to increase the length of a rope to 50 metres?

F What is the maximum number of people who can be seated in a theatre having 72 seats in each of 25 rows?

G If a bottle of school milk contains 200 ml, what quantity of milk is needed to supply the school with 345 bottles each day during the school week—Monday to Friday?

H A car should travel 56 kilometres on 10 litres of petrol.   How many litres should be needed on a tour of 980 kilometres?

I How long should you be away from home if you live a twenty minute journey from the station, catch a train at 10.15 and return by a train which should arrive at 16.50?

J If hymn books are £2·50 each, find how many can be bought for £10·00?

K Draw a right angle triangle so that, of the two sides which are perpendicular to each other, one is 12 cm and the other is 9 cm. What is the length of the third side?

L Ann noticed that on the first day she read $\frac{2}{5}$ of the pages in a book and $\frac{1}{3}$ on the second day.   If the book contained 240 pages how many pages were left for the third day?